RUTH McKENNEY

D1083923

My Sister Eileen

HARCOURT, BRACE & WORLD, INC.

NEW YORK

The contents of this book are reprinted from *The
New Yorker*, through the courtesy of the editors.

Designed by Robert Josephy
PRINTED IN THE UNITED STATES OF AMERICA

FOR EILEEN

with love

I wish to thank Katharine S. White, one of the editors of *The New Yorker*, for the great help she gave me in preparing these stories for publication.

FOREWORD

THIS BOOK is a considerably censored account of the awful things my sister Eileen and I lived through when we were growing up.

The reason it is censored is because nobody will believe the very worst things that happened to Eileen and me during our tender years. "Pooh," people yell at me when I try to explain why Eileen and I spent a whole summer in a deserted monastery in Columbus, Ohio, fighting a brood of oversized and somewhat insane bats. The bats used to come out on moonlit nights, from the hole in a telephone pole where they ordinarily lived in cozy seclusion. On their moon-crazed expeditions, they always headed directly for our little hideaway in the monastery and flew around our bed making nasty whirring sounds. Finally, we got some screens but then the bats, determined creatures that they were, sat on the window sill, father bat and mother bat and six child bats, trying to gnaw their way through the wire into our bower. It was very nerve-racking. But of course nobody will believe it.

Or cynical listeners bawl, "G'wan," in accents rude and sneering when Eileen and I laughingly recall a kindly, but, as they say, crusty old ferry-boat captain we knew (name on request to right parties). This salty mariner, eighty-nine years young, dreamed of drowning all the passengers on the 5:15 express to Staten Island. I guess certain of our friends who believe all they hear about ferry-boat captains in sentimental plays like "Excursion" will have a mighty rude awakening if that ferry-boat captain ever runs amuck and fulfills the ambition of a lifetime. The reason he wants to drown a lot of people is that he hates people. He liked them all right until he took to ferry-boating seventy years ago, but his opinion of the human race has gradually tapered off, with years of meeting ferry-boat passengers. Now he can just barely stand his wife, who is really a sweet old soul and bakes a mean cherry pie. It is only a matter of time, Eileen and I think, until the big debacle. Unless, of course, he gets pensioned off first.

Well, this gives you an idea. Most of the things that happened to Eileen and me in our youth, and keep right on happening for that matter, are rejected by the ordinary little-minded person as a lot of hog-wash, to put it crudely.

So the following account of the Life and Sufferings of the McKenney sisters is, I admit, pretty watered down. I trust, therefore, that the reader will find it at least faintly credible. For it's all true, no matter how terrible.

R. McK.

CONTENTS

xi

CONTENTS

CONTENTS

No Tears, No Good

WHICH IS AN ACCOUNT OF HOW MY SISTER
EILEEN AND I WENT TO THE MOVIES.

THE nicely brought up child of today lives on a prissy milk-and-water movie diet of colored cartoons, costume pictures with noble endings, and banal dramas starring his favorite radio comic. The Mickey Mouse vogue among the juniors demonstrates what fearful changes Will Hays, the Legion of Decency, and Aroused Parenthood have wrought in a mere twenty years or so.

My sister Eileen and I, movie fans when we were five and six, respectively, would have scorned Mickey Mouse in our youth; we preferred Theda Bara to Fatty Arbuckle, and that was the acid test.

We saw our first movie shortly after we saw our first airplane. The airplane was very nice, of course, and we had a school half-holiday to celebrate the glorious moment when an air machine first put landing gear on the dreary soil of Mishawaka, Indiana. That was the early spring of 1918, and airplanes were very patriotic and thrilling, but in spite of the glamorous fellow who ran the queer machine, we liked the movie better than the airplane. The movie lasted longer.

Our first film was Chapter 3 of a serial which had to do with bandits, high cliffs, and pistols. Eileen was so small she was able to sneak under the ticket-seller's high box and get in free. The serial was shown that spring daily, not weekly, in a made-over garage not far from our schoolhouse. Chapter 1 of the adventures of, say, Death-Defying Desmond started on Monday at four o'clock sharp and the last installment ended at the Friday-afternoon matinée, amid the hoarse cheers of the excited audience. Admission price was a nickel, but no self-respecting child in our fairly prosperous neighborhood would have thought of stumbling down the dark aisles and throwing himself into a creaking wooden seat unless he were equipped with a bag of peanuts, price also five cents.

The peanuts were not merely for the inner man; the shells were used by the large and energetic audience to enliven the dull stretches in the scenario. To us, even the liveliest Western had a good many sleepy sequences, and, indeed, the whole audience could be bored into mass fidgets at the mere sight of a long subtitle, for few, if any, of the paying customers at those four-o'clock matinées could read— not, at least, with any ease. Nobody in the theatre had the slightest idea of what the film was about, and nobody cared. We came to see the fights, and the horse races over the mountains, and the jumping across chasms. Our attention wandered as soon as the

4

scene shifted indoors, and two subtitles in a row were enough to start a peanut fight.

Thus, when the heroine began to plead with the villain for the hero's life, Benny Burns, a big boy in the third grade, would rise and shoot a peanut shell at his old enemy, Freddie Meriman. Freddie would respond in kind, and soon the darkened theatre would be the scene of a fine free-for-all battle, with both sides eventually running out of peanut shells and resorting to books, hats, apples, and other deadly weapons. Piercing screams could sometimes be heard all the way out to the street, and the howls of the wounded would sooner or later seriously annoy the bored movie operator, upstairs in his booth. He and the ticket-seller were the only attendants, for in those days there were no laws about matrons, and for a nickel we did not have the dubious pleasure of hearing the regular pianist. In the midst of the joyous battle, then, the lights would suddenly go on, the heroine disappear from the screen, and the racket diminish slightly while the operator bawled, "Shut up, you brats, or I'll throw you all out."

"Ya-a-ah," we would all scream, Eileen's five-year-old shriek rising above the rest, "come on and do it!"

5

He never tried, though. He waited for comparative quiet, dimmed the lights, and put the heroine back on the screen, this time perhaps pleading, in one of those lightning developments, for her own life. The peanut battles were apparently more exciting than the serials. I remember little of that first spring movie season except a train wreck, but that train wreck will live in my memory as one of the most piquant experiences of my life.

In the film, a motorcar, a Model T Ford, was racing down a country road, pursued by something—I think it was a lot of bandits in another car. Just as the motorcar approached the crossing, a train appeared around a convenient bend. All this was old stuff; we were used to seeing motorcars and trains fight it out on the tracks.

But suddenly the camera switched from the general view of the automobile and the train, and on the screen appeared a huge pair of wheels—the train wheels. They grew larger and larger, revolving furiously. We were awed and horrified. The wheels were coming right for us; apparently, the motorcar was not to be run over, we were. Suddenly my sister Eileen screamed, and began trying to climb across the tense legs of the little boys in our row.

"Let me out, let me out!" she howled. "Ruth! Mamma! Help! It's coming!"

In the silence of the darkened movie house, Eileen's screams made a sensation. Other small girls burst into nervous sobs. Boys, even big boys in the third grade, began to whine dismally. On the screen the wheels were now rolling faster and faster, and the whole train loomed up, apparently about to descend upon us. In those days, when a cameraman had a good shot, he gave it plenty of footage, to let it sink in. Eileen's agonized howls and cries for help were now being drowned out by the panic-stricken roar of the whole audience. There was a tremendous din, and the scuffle of dozens of frightened children trying to stumble out into the aisles and run for home and mother. At this point the lights went on and the train, wheels and all, disappeared from the screen.

"For Christ's sake!" bawled the infuriated movie operator from his booth. The attention of the horrified audience was now shifted from the thought of escape, to horror at hearing a bad word, a swear word, shouted so baldly from above. This was a polite neighborhood.

"This ain't real," the movie operator continued in

his stentorian tones. "Nobody's going to get hurt. It's just a movie."

You could hear the soft rustle of everybody saying "Oh" to his neighbor, the diminishing sniffles, the blowing of noses, the regaining of creaking wooden seats. But before the lights went down, the ticket-seller, a mean-looking lady of what we thought was vast age, with side puffs over her ears, walked down the aisle.

"Who started this?" she demanded sternly. A dozen fingers pointed to my fat, tear-stained sister. Eileen tried to hide under her seat, but in vain. She was ordered out to the aisle.

"How old are you?" the ticket-seller demanded, in front of everybody.

"Theven," Eileen lied, in her most unfortunate lisp. A dozen voices contradicted her. "She's only in kindergarten," various old pals shouted gleefully.

"Little girls in kindergarten aren't allowed to come to the movies," the ticket-seller said grimly, and grabbed Eileen's chubby arm. Weeping dismally, my poor sister was ignominiously led out, with me tagging sorrowfully along in back. Unfortunately, this event made such a scandal that our mother heard of it, via other little girls' mothers, and we were forbidden to attend movies until we were older.

Older was next year, after we had moved to Cleveland. There were three movie houses within walking distance of our new home, and we settled down to delightful years of Saturday and Sunday afternoon film orgies.

Nobody censored our movie fare except ourselves. Mother had no idea of what grim and gripping pictures we were seeing, for she never went to the movies herself. She was something of an intellectual, and back in 1919 and 1920 people who had pretensions to culture, at least in the Middle West, wouldn't have been caught dead in a movie house. Mother thought the films were exclusively for children and morons, like the comic strips in the newspapers. Cleveland had no Better Films for Children Committees in those days, and Ohio preachers and newspaper editorial-writers did not thunder, then, of the Movie Menace. Mother used to send us off to the neighborhood theatres with an innocent and loving heart.

"Don't sit through it more than twice!" she would shout from the front porch as we skipped off, hand in hand, to the movies. We would return, hours

9

later, exhausted from the hard seats and emotional duress.

We saw some bright and cheerful pictures, but I don't remember many of them. There was Fatty Arbuckle, of course, and two wonderful children who threw dishes at each other—the Lee sisters. We worshiped them. But most of the pictures we saw were, to us anyway, grim and awful tragedies. If there were happy endings, we never noticed them. Some of the pictures were so unbearably sad we could hardly stay to see them twice. We did, though.

We wore large, round hats with ribbons for these excursions to the movies. Once settled down in our seats, we held on anxiously to the hats. At the least sign of trouble on the screen, we put the hats in front of our eyes. Then we took turns peeking out to see if the film had taken a turn for the better. It makes me blanch to consider what we would have suffered if the films had been wired for sound when we were children. As it was, we could generally tell when the trouble was coming by the pianist, who used to begin thumping away at some very dread music. Of course, since we saw every film twice, in spite of our hat system of censorship we generally got the thread of the plot on the second time around. If we still couldn't quite make out what had happened, we stayed for the third show and were late for dinner.

We had no favorite movie stars at first, for the truth was that we hadn't really believed that movie operator. For a long time we thought the movies were real, and that the tragedies we saw were photographed, mysteriously, from real and horrible life. I gradually came to understand that the suffering heroine was only an actress and I used to reassure Eileen loudly as she wept. "Don't cry," I would bawl through my own tears. "It's only a movie."

At last, though, we grew out of this primitive stage of movie response and developed into Wally Reid and Lon Chaney fans. Mr. Chaney, of course, we admired in a rather backhanded way. Each Chaney film was, for us, a terrible ordeal, through which we suffered and bawled and wept. As we staggered out of the theatre, our pug noses swollen to red beets, we swore never to set eyes on the man again. But the next time we were back, groaning in our seats, fascinated and horrified. Finally "The Hunchback of Notre Dame" came along and very nearly finished me off. Even now, Eileen refuses to discuss that gruesome movie. Mr. Chaney was the hunchback, of course. and he suffered a peculiarly realistic and horrible beating in that old silent film. Eileen and I put our arms around each other, and howled steadily throughout the entire beating.

Mr. Reid, who came along a little earlier than the horror man, was a slightly more cheerful influence on our childhood, although his tragic death became, oddly enough, a family scandal. Our passion for Mr. Reid was shared by a young aunt of ours, who admired that jaunty actor with rather more enthusiasm than detachment. Now, my mother cared nothing for Mr. Reid but she was deeply attached to her only brother and she called him, as Mr. Reid's devoted fans called their idol, Wally.

Imagine her horror, then, one evening, when my young aunt called up and wept over the phone, in broken accents, "Maggie, Maggie, Wally's dead!"

"Dead?" shouted my mother, electrifying everybody at our dinner table. "No! No! It isn't true!"

My aunt said, amid her tears, that it was true, alas. My mother began, naturally enough, to cry. My father, white and shaken, rushed to the phone, tenderly pushed his wife aside while she sobbed, "Wally's dead," and picked up the receiver.

"How did it happen?" Father began, in that somber tone of voice you use for these trying occasions.

Then we heard him roar, "What? You're crazy!"
He hung up with a frightful bang and shouted, "It's
Wally Reid, the film actor!"

Eileen and I began to howl at once. We didn't
know our uncle very well, but we certainly knew
Wally Reid, and felt perfectly terrible about his
death. We simply couldn't understand Mother's
calloused revival when she heard the good news that
her brother still lived. That famous telephone conversation started a family feud that lasted for years.
Mother never forgave her young sister, and my aunt
stated freely and frankly that she thought Mother
was a perfect idiot for not knowing that Wally Reid
had been ill for days. People took their movies seriously those days, if they took them at all.

In spite of our devotion to Mr. Chaney and Mr.
Reid, the film that made the deepest impression
upon Eileen and myself when we were nine and ten
or thereabouts starred neither of these gentlemen.
The name of the film I never knew. We paid no
attention to such trifles as titles, directors or the
names of the cast. We saw it in a third-run house in
the fall or late summer of 1921.

The movie opened with a charming domestic
scene. The newly married wife was saving nickels

for her Home. She had a special bank, made like a little house, for the purpose. But suddenly a handsome villain appeared on the scene, a business acquaintance of her husband. He invited the happy couple to a very swell party, and the little woman needed a new dress. So she pried open the quaint little bank (while Eileen squirmed and cried, "No, no!" in a perfect agony) and bought a wonderful dress for three hundred dollars. The couple trotted off to the party, the wife feeling pretty guilty of course, while the husband, the fool, bridled with pride. He told everyone who would listen to him that his wife's lovely gown was home-made by the clever little woman herself. How heartlessly Eileen and I laughed at that. We had no sympathy for the spineless husband; he was an oaf. Now the wife had planned to wear the gown but a single night and rush it back to the dress shop the next morning. Then she would put the money back in the cute little bank and her husband would never be the wiser. Eileen and I thought that was pretty risky. We always spilled things at parties, ourselves.

Sure enough, the party turned out to be a debauch. We weren't surprised. All grown-up parties were, in our opinion, debauches, and we were sure our parents, when they left the house in evening clothes, were bound for similar sinful sprees. This party, however, was a humdinger. It was climaxed by all the guests' tearing out of doors to go swimming in the ocean *with their clothes on*. We wouldn't have minded if they had gone in naked. We thought first and last of that three-hundred-dollar dress.

Eileen cried so at this point that the usher had to rebuke her; her sobs were distracting the pianist. We had our hats up, of course, but we were so stirred by the tragedy we couldn't help sneak looks at the screen. There she was, wading in; there she was, going in deeper. Then—oh, fearful tragedy!—a wave broke over her head and the dress was a goner. I forget how the movie ended. The husband found out and beat up his poor wife, I believe.

Rudolph Valentino came next in our movie career. We were having our teeth straightened when the Great Lover burst into our lives. We must have missed his early films or, worse, sat through them without a quiver, for we were twelve and thirteen before we began to take Mr. Valentino seriously, and then his career was very nearly over. But even so, I feel genuinely sorry for modern adolescents to think that their first sighs cannot be wasted on Rudolph

Valentino. Alas, how much grosser is Clark Gable, how much milder is Robert Taylor! Ah, I can see, I can practically feel, Mr. Valentino's arms sliding and slithering around his prey; I can see his wonderful profile coming closer, bit by bit, his lips quivering, his eyes gleaming with that snake-eat-bird expression. Ah!

We saw Mr. Valentino's last film, "The Son of the Sheik," released in Cleveland after his death, six times all the way through and came back a seventh time just for the desert love scene. In those days no prudish censor cut the romantic footage, and we sighed gustily while the heroine struggled in the Great Lover's arms. We disliked that heroine, whoever she was, very much indeed. We thought it was both disloyal and stupid of her to put up a fight against Mr. Valentino. We would have given in at once.

When "The Big Parade" came to Cleveland, a year or so later, we were old enough to see the movies in the big downtown houses, providing, of course, that we had the cash. I remember we got the money to see "The Big Parade," in the best seats of the legitimate theatre showing the film, by coolly calling on the credit manager of a department store where our father had an account. With lowered eyes and swinging pigtails, we told him we were stranded; we had lost our purses. Would he please advance us four dollars for taxi fare home? He was stunned, apparently, by this novel approach, for he handed over the money and we rushed out, bought a two-pound box of the best chocolate-nut candy, and descended upon "The Big Parade."

Tragedies of a very real nature have overtaken us both since that spring day, but we have never cried so, either of us, again. We wept buckets. We wept through our own handkerchiefs, which, for a change, we had remembered. We wept through the ruffles on our petticoats. When we started to sob on the back of our hands, a sympathetic gentleman sitting next to me gallantly offered his large handkerchief, and we wept together on that as the orchestra (this was a very special performance) played "My Buddy" and the guns thundered and the cast died, on the screen. Afterward we agreed it was the best movie we had ever seen, because we had cried the most. Our standard was simple but severe. No tears, no good.

"The Big Parade" was the last picture belonging to the idyllic, or honeymoon, stage of the movies for us. After that, our high-school beaux began to buy our movie tickets, and for many years, alas, the beaux took up more of our attention than the movies. By the time we had recovered from the shock of not paying our own way in, we were living in New York City and reading the *Times* moving-picture reviews. And somehow the movies have never been the same for us as they were in the days when we saw them in snatches from behind our big, round hats.

Hun-gah

WHEN my sister and I were ten and eleven, our six aunts on the lace-curtain-Irish, or Farrel, side of the family got up a little fund to make their nieces cultured.

In their dreams, they could see, these amiable ladies who loved us so dearly, Eileen at the piano bringing tears to the eyes of her relatives with a splendid performance of "Narcissus," the selection where you cross your hands on the keyboard. They could see me, too, in their affectionate musings, spreading a fluffy organdie skirt for a polite curtsy to a parlor full of admiring Farrels and Murphys and Flannigans, and then launching into a moving recitation of "Trees."

After all, our second cousins, the Murphy children, aged only eleven and twelve, could already recite "Trees" and play "The Rose of No Man's Land," not to speak of "Humoresque," on the piano. If the Murphys could be cultured, so, my aunts said grimly, could the McKenneys. If they had secret misgivings, they never said so. They started off the big culture program by getting Eileen a music teacher, a nervous, angular lady who wore her eyeglasses on a black ribbon and sniffled.

"One," she used to say, "two, three," and then a

long sniffle, "four. One, two," then another short, ladylike sniffle, "three, four."

The sniffles and the black ribbon for the eyeglasses fascinated my sister. She used to keep time to the sniffles instead of the counting, and as a result her scales went from bad to worse. Eventually, though, she learned to read simple sheet music. She also learned a bass which consisted mostly of fearful thumping and a rolling sound like kettledrums, all in the lowest octave of the keyboard. With this equipment, she was able to play "Chloe," a popular song of the early nineteen-twenties. She was never able to play anything except "Chloe," but she certainly could play that.

She used to stalk to the piano and seat herself firmly, with quite a thump, at the bench. Then, swaying largely from the waist, she picked up the melody, not without some difficulty. Finally, when the preliminaries were over, she burst into song, accompanying herself as she went along.

"Thr—ooo the bu-la-ck of NIGHT," Eileen used to intone in a deep bass growl, "I got-tuh go wheah yew ARE."

The climax of the song, where the melody goes up, always used to baffle my poor sister, who, like myself, is absolutely tone-deaf and has never been able to carry a tune, even the simplest one, in her whole life. She solved the difficulty by simply pounding so hard in the bass that she drowned herself out. Her voice emerged triumphantly just at the end: "I GOT-TUH go wheah yew ARE."

While Eileen was learning to play a bayou chant, I, too, was busy with culture. I was taking what my aunts thought were elocution lessons. These thoughtful ladies, after a solemn family conclave, had decided I should study public speaking because I stuttered over the telephone. I still do. It is very humiliating.

How my conservative, respectable aunts fell afoul of Madame DuLak and her Studio of the Voice I cannot imagine. Certainly she was not the teacher they thought she was. They hoped that I would learn how to recite "Trees." Madame DuLak told me the first time I met her that Joyce Kilmer "stank." That was the word she used. I was eleven years old, and I certainly was surprised to hear that about Joyce Kilmer.

Madame DuLak had studied in Paris. She said so often. She had picked up a lot of fancy notions in gay old Paris, I gathered, not only about Joyce Kilmer but also about "recitations" and "elocution lessons."

"We are going," Madame DuLak intoned, in a rich, deep voice full of culture, that first morning our little class of six assembled, "to undertake the study of a litt-tul play which I rather" (she said "rawther," of course) "like. I shall assign and read the parts this morning. By next week you will have memorized your lines, and then we shall settle down for a winter's work."

I memorized my lines easily. My part consisted of the word "hunger." But do not imagine that I was a mere walk-on in this little play of Madame DuLak's. On the contrary, I was one of the leading characters. I was, in spite my rotund figure, a hungry old beggar. I sat on the steps of what was supposed to be a cathedral. From the time the curtain went up until at last it went down, I sat on those steps, chanting the word "hunger" more or less at one-minute intervals. Sometimes I said it very loudly, drowning out the rest of the cast, and sometimes I was supposed to whisper it very softly, as background. It was a Greek-chorus idea.

The play was exceedingly symbolical. I was not supposed to be physically hungry, which was a good thing, considering my appearance; I was just supposed to be spiritually hungry. Madame DuLak used to urge me to put this difference into the reading of my lines, or, rather, line. I was a big girl for my eleven years, and I was often hungry in the good old-fashioned sense of wanting another piece of chocolate cake or second helping of chocolate pie. So when Madame DuLak would urge me on Saturday mornings to "Put some *feeling* into your part, Ruth," I would concentrate hard on something chocolate and howl, "Hun-gah!" with a fine frenzied note in my voice. Madame DuLak thought I was pretty good, on the whole. Of course sometimes I forgot and said, "Hunger," and then Madame DuLak used to denounce me as a boor.

The rest of the pupils were also symbolical. The only other girl in the class, Betty Chippendale, was Vice. I wanted to be Vice myself; I got pretty tired of being a dirty old beggar yelling, "Hun-gah!" all the time. Vice was a nice, rich part. There weren't any lines in the part, to be sure, not even a one-word chant like my "Hun-gah," but Vice got to stroll up and down the stage, wiggling her hips, brushing against other characters with lewd gestures, and such like. Of course Betty was only thirteen years old, and although she wanted to be an actress when she grew

25

up, her life had been rather restricted so far. So she had some difficulty in making her character study of Vice symbolical enough to suit Madame DuLak.

"No, no, Betty," Madame DuLak would say in her cultured voice, "you represent the dregs of humanity, you are the symbol of lust and ugliness. You must make your audience feel that as you move across the stage, you must put that into every gesture of your little finger."

"Yes, Ma'am," Betty would say. She took her work very seriously, and never got tired of walking up and down and being the symbol of lust and ugliness.

The boys were, variously, Greed and Power and Truth and Loving Kindness. Since this was a pretty modern morality play, Loving Kindness and Truth got licked to a frazzle at the curtain. Greed and Power beat them up and dragged them off bodily every Saturday morning. Vice tagged along to get in on the kill, and that left me still sitting on the cathedral steps. I had the last lines. "Hun-gah!" I bellowed. "Hun-gah! Hun-gah!" Curtain.

I think now that Madame DuLak must have written that remarkable play herself. Of course it had certain resemblances to other dramas of its genre, but that smashing finish—that was pure DuLak.

After the first three weeks, Madame DuLak decided we must have costumes for our rehearsals. The costumes, she said, would help us get into the feeling of our roles. My costume was wonderful. I made it myself, and it certainly was realistic. I wore an old, ragged, burlap sack with holes cut out for the arms. My legs were bare, and I had a pair of Father's old bedroom slippers tied on my feet with rope. This was only the beginning, however. I took off my hair ribbon, unbraided my pigtails, and systematically, with a comb, snarled and matted my long hair. Then I covered my face, arms, and legs with artistic smatterings of coal dust. The first time Madame DuLak saw me emerge from my dressing room in her little studio, she gave me the highest praise a make-up artist can get.

"Awk!" she said, blasted out of her usual cultured calm.

With the first soft breezes of spring, with the first robin, my aunts began to question me rather sharply about my elocution lessons. I explained as well as I could about the play, but I could see that they rejected my story as the simple fantasy of an imaginative child. They urged me to recite my part for them, but some inner instinct warned me off.

Finally, though, one of the Farrel family reunions came along. The Farrels had family reunions at the drop of a hat, and the Murphys, the Flannigans, the McKenneys, Aunt Susan Maloney with her brood, and assorted other in-laws turned up, ate prodigiously, and argued about politics. Our aunts felt that it was practically certain that the Murphy girls would play "The Rose of No Man's Land" and recite "Trees."

"This time," Aunt Molly said, with a dangerous glitter in her eye, "we'll show them that the Murphy girls aren't the only ones in the family who take lessons."

Eileen and I turned up at the family reunion bearing our stage properties. I brought my costume in a box, with a neat bag of coal dust, and Eileen brought the sheet music of "Chloe." We weren't nervous in the least. After dinner we retired upstairs to prepare for what we felt would be our triumph. Eileen gargled, and I repeated "Hun-gah, hun-gah" several times, to get in voice.

Downstairs we could hear Margaret Murphy playing "The Rose of No Man's Land," and very badly, too. She had to start over again several times. The applause, however, was generous.

When Cousin Rita Murphy began to recite "Trees," Uncle Wally went out to the kitchen, and we heard him say, "There is a limit to everything, Katie. Where do they keep the whiskey bottle around here?" Katie was the cook. We bridled. Uncle Wally would never walk out on *our* performances, we felt sure.

He didn't. Nobody did. They were frozen to their seats. We got, in fact, the most flattering kind of attention. Even Uncle Wally's jaws fell ajar.

Eileen played and sang first. Just as the final notes of her bass monotone chant, "I GOT-TUH go wheah yew ARE," and the final rumble of the piano died away, I burst dramatically through the door, shouting "Hun-gah! Hun-gah!" and shaking my matted and snarled locks at my assembled relatives. My grandmother Farrel, who always takes everything seriously, let out a piercing scream.

Ignoring the awed comments of the rest of the audience, I paced slowly over to the fireplace. "This," I said in stately tones, while my aunts stared at my coal-dust-streaked face, "is a cathedral. I am sitting on the cathedral steps." I sat down. There was a long pause. Then I put up my arms to the heavens.

"Hun-gah!" I shrieked. Grandma jumped and said audibly, "Mercy!"

I let another impressive silence fall. The Murphys, mother and father and the two accomplished child Murphys, breathed heavily. Suddenly I plopped down on the floor, my face turned to the horrified audience.

"Hun-gah," I barely breathed. Eileen struck a soft chord in the bass.

"God!" Uncle Wally said. In the silence, everybody heard him, but they were too engrossed in my performance to be shocked. I rolled over, one limp hand trailing on the carpet.

"Hun-gah!" I whined. I lay on the floor several seconds, letting it sink in. Then I began to drag myself to my feet. My knee joints always cracked, and in the silence you could hear them clearly all over the room. Nobody said anything. Finally I was all the way up, and panting. I was supposed to pant. I was supposed to have some kind of a terrible disease, like leprosy. I lowered my head, inch by inch. In those days I had a double chin, and I couldn't get my head down very far, unfortunately. I sighed, heavily.

Then in a flat, sad voice I said, "Hun-gah."

Eileen struck a minor chord. I bowed. I stalked toward the door. Eileen rose gravely and followed me. At the door we bowed together.

"Well, for God's sake!" my Uncle Wally said, quite loudly. We waited for the burst of applause, but our relatives sat glued to their seats, staring at us. Finally Aunt Molly pulled herself together and started to clap. Everybody else clapped too, dutifully, and we retired with the sweet sound of applause in our ears.

There never was another family reunion like that one. We knew perfectly well we had electrified our dear relatives. As Eileen put it, "It was about time somebody stuck a pin in them." Anyway, Uncle Wally told us afterward that he liked us better than "Trees." He thought that we had done it on purpose, and maybe, as I look back on it, we did. Our approach to life was somewhat confused at ten and eleven.

After that, the Murphy girls had the field of culture, in our family, to themselves. It never did them any good, either.

A Loud Sneer for Our Feathered Friends

WE GO TO A GIRLS' CAMP AND DON'T THINK
MUCH OF IT. ALSO ABOUT BIRDS.

FROM childhood, my sister and I have had a well-grounded dislike for our friends the birds. We came to hate them when she was ten and I was eleven. We had been exiled by what we considered an unfeeling family to one of those loathsome girls' camps where Indian lore is rife and the management puts up neatly lettered signs reminding the clients to be Good Sports. From the moment Eileen and I arrived at dismal old Camp Hi-Wah, we were Bad Sports, and we liked it.

We refused to get out of bed when the bugle blew in the morning, we fought against scrubbing our teeth in public to music, we sneered when the flag was ceremoniously lowered at sunset, we avoided doing a good deed a day, we complained loudly about the food, which was terrible, and we bought some chalk once and wrote all over the Recreation Cabin, "We hate Camp Hi-Wah." It made a wonderful scandal, although unfortunately we were immediately accused of the crime. All the other little campers *loved* dear old Camp Hi-Wah, which shows you what kind of people they were.

The first two weeks Eileen and I were at Camp Hi-Wah, we sat in our cabin grinding our teeth at our councilor and writing letters to distant relatives. These letters were, if I say so myself, real master-

35

pieces of double dealing and heartless chicanery. In our childish and, we hoped, appealing scrawl, we explained to Great-Aunt Mary Farrel and Second Cousin Joe Murphy that we were having such fun at dear Camp Hi-Wah making Indian pocketbooks.

"We would simply l-o-v-e to make you a pocket-book, dear Aunt Mary," we wrote, "only the leather costs $1 for a small pocketbook or $1.67 for a large size pocketbook, which is much nicer because you can carry more things in it, and the rawhide you sew it up with, just exactly the way the Indians did, costs 40 cents more. We burn pictures on the leather but that doesn't cost anything. If we o-n-l-y had $1 or $1.67 and 40 cents for the rawhide, we could make you the s-w-e-l-l-e-s-t pocketbook."

As soon as we had enough orders for Indian pocketbooks with pictures burnt on them, we planned to abscond with the funds sent by our trusting relatives and run away to New York City, where, as we used to explain dramatically to our cabin-mates, we intended to live a life of sin. After a few days, our exciting plans for our immediate future were bruited all over the camp, and admirers came from as far away as Cabin Minnehaha, which was way down at the end of Hiawatha Alley, just to hear us tell about New York and sin.

Fame had its price, however. One of the sweet little girls who lived in our cabin turned out to be such a Good Citizen ("Camp Hi-Wah Girls Learn to Be Good Citizens") that she told our dreadful secret to our councilor. Our mail was impounded for weeks, and worst of all, we actually had to make several Indian pocketbooks with pictures burnt on them. My pictures were all supposed to be snakes, although they were pretty blurred. Eileen specialized in what she believed to be the likeness of a werewolf, but Cousin Joe, who had generously ordered three pocketbooks, wrote a nice letter thanking Eileen for his pretty pocketbooks with the pretty pictures of Abraham Lincoln on them. We were terribly disgusted by the whole thing.

It was in this mood that we turned to birds. The handicraft hour at Camp Hi-Wah, heralded by the ten-thirty A.M. bugle, competed for popularity with the bird walks at the same hour. You could, as Eileen had already somewhat precociously learned how to say, name your own poison. After three weeks of burning pictures on leather, we were ready for anything, even our feathered friends.

37

So one hot morning in July, the two McKenney sisters, big and bad and fierce for their age, answered the bird-walk bugle call, leaving the Indian-pocket-book teacher to mourn her two most backward pupils. We were dressed, somewhat reluctantly, to be sure, in the required heavy stockings for poison ivy and brambles, and carried, each of us, in our dirty hands a copy of a guide to bird lore called *Bird Life for Children.*

Bird Life for Children was a volume that all the Good Citizens in Camp Hi-Wah pretended to find engrossing. Eileen and I thought it was stupefyingly dull. Our favorite literary character at the time was Dumas' Marguerite de Valois, who took her decapitated lover's head home in a big handkerchief for old times' sake. Eileen, in those days, was always going to name her first girl child Marguerite de Valois.

Bird Life for Children was full of horrid pictures in full color of robins and pigeons and redbirds. Under each picture was a loathsomely whimsical paragraph describing how the bird in question spent his spare time, what he ate, and why children should love him. Eileen and I hated the book so, we were quite prepared to despise birds when we started off that morning on our first bird walk, but we had no idea of what we were going to suffer, that whole awful summer, because of our feathered friends. In the first place, since we had started off making leather pocketbooks, we were three weeks behind the rest of the Hi-Wah bird-lovers. They had been tramping through blackberry bushes for days and days and had already got the hang of the more ordinary bird life around camp, whereas the only bird I could identify at the time was the vulture. Cousin Joe took me to a zoo once, and there was a fine vulture there, a big, fat one. They fed him six live rats every day in lieu of human flesh. I kept a sharp eye out for a vulture all summer, but one never turned up at Camp Hi-Wah. Nothing interesting ever happened around that place.

On that first bird walk, Eileen and I trotted anxiously along behind the little band of serious-minded bird-lovers, trying desperately to see, or at least hear, even one bird, even one robin. But alas, while other bird-walkers saw, or pretended to see—for Eileen and I never believed them for a moment—all kinds of hummingbirds and hawks and owls and whatnot, we never saw or heard a single, solitary feathered friend, not one.

39

By the time we staggered into camp for lunch, with stubbed toes, scratched faces, and tangled hair, Eileen and I were soured for life on birds. Our bird logs, which we carried strapped to our belts along with the *Guide*, were still chaste and bare, while all the other little bird-lovers had fulsome entries, such as "Saw and heard redbird at 10:37 A.M. Molting."

Still, for the next three days we stayed honest and suffered. For three terrible mornings we endured being dolts among bird-walkers, the laughing-stock of Camp Hi-Wah. After six incredibly tiresome hours, our bird logs were still blank. Then we cracked under the strain. The fourth morning we got up feeling grim but determined. We sharpened our pencils before we started off on the now-familiar trail through the second-growth forest.

When we got well into the woods and Mary Mahoney, the premier bird-walker of Camp Hi-Wah, had already spotted and logged her first redbird of the morning, Eileen suddenly stopped dead in her tracks. "Hark!" she cried. She had read that somewhere in a book. "Quiet!" I echoed instantly.

The bird-walkers drew to a halt respectfully and stood in silence. They stood and stood. It was not good form even to whisper while fellow bird-walkers were logging a victim, but after quite a long time the Leader, whose feet were flat and often hurt her, whispered impatiently, "Haven't you got him logged yet?"

"You drove him away," Eileen replied sternly. "It was a yellow-billed cuckoo."

"A yellow-billed cuckoo?" cried the Leader incredulously.

"Well," Eileen said modestly, "at least *I* think it was." Then, with many a pretty hesitation and thoughtful pause, she recited the leading features of the yellow-billed cuckoo, as recorded in *Bird Life for Children*.

The Leader was terribly impressed. Later on that morning I logged a kingfisher, a red-headed woodpecker, and a yellow-bellied sapsucker, which was all I could remember at the moment. Each time, I kept the bird-walkers standing around for an interminable period, gaping into blank space and listening desperately to the rustle of the wind in the trees and the creak of their shoes as they went from one foot to another.

In a few days Eileen and I were the apple of our Leader's eye, the modest heroes of the Camp Hi-

Wah bird walks. Naturally, there were base children around camp, former leading bird-walkers, who spread foul rumors up and down Hiawatha Alley that Eileen and I were frauds. We soon stopped this ugly talk, however. Eileen was the pitcher, and a very good one, too, of the Red Bird ball team and I was the first base. When Elouise Pritchard, the worst gossip in Cabin Sitting Bull, came up to bat, she got a pitched ball right in the stomach. Of course it was only a soft ball, but Eileen could throw it pretty hard. To vary this routine, I tagged Mary Mahoney, former head bird-walker, out at first base, and Mary had a bruise on her thigh for weeks. The rumors stopped abruptly.

We had begun to get pretty bored with logging rare birds when the game took on a new angle. Mary Mahoney and several other bird-walkers began to see the same birds we did on our morning jaunts into the forest. This made us pretty mad, but there wasn't much we could do about it. Next, Mary Mahoney began to see birds we weren't logging. The third week after we joined the Camp Hi-Wah Bird Study Circle, everybody except the poor, dumb Leader and a few backward but honest bird-lovers was logging the rarest birds seen around Camp Hi-Wah in twenty years. Bird walks developed into a race to see who could shout "Hark!" first and keep the rest of the little party in fidgety silence for the next five minutes.

The poor bird-walk Leader was in agony. Her reputation as a bird-lover was in shreds. Her talented pupils were seeing rare birds right and left, while the best she could log for herself would be a few crummy old redbirds and a robin or so. At last our Leader's morale collapsed. It was the day when nearly everybody in the study circle swore that she saw and heard a bona-fide nightingale.

"Where?" cried our Leader desperately, after the fourth nightingale had been triumphantly logged in the short space of five minutes. Heartless fingers pointed to a vague bush. The Leader strained her honest eyes. No notion of our duplicity crossed her innocent, unworldly mind.

"I can't see any nightingale," our Leader cried, and burst into tears. Then, full of shame, she sped back to camp, leaving the Camp Hi-Wah bird-lovers to their nightingales and guilty thoughts.

Eileen and I ate a hearty lunch that noon because we thought we would need it. Then we strolled

43

down Hiawatha Alley and hunted up Mary Mahoney.

"We will put the Iron Cross on you if you tell," Eileen started off, as soon as we found Mary.

"What's the Iron Cross?" Mary squeaked, startled out of her usual haughty poise.

"Never mind," I growled. "You'll find out if you tell."

We walked past Cabin Sitting Bull, past the flagpole, into the tall grass beyond the ball field.

"She'll tell," Eileen said finally.

"What'll we do?" I replied mournfully. "They'll try us at campfire tonight."

They did, too. It was terrible. We denied everything, but the Head of Camp, a mean old lady who wore middy blouses and pleated serge bloomers, sentenced us to no desserts and eight-o'clock bedtime for two weeks. We thought over what to do to Mary Mahoney for four whole days. Nothing seemed sufficiently frightful, but in the end we put the wart curse on her. The wart curse was simple but horrible. We dropped around to Cabin Sitting Bull one evening and in the presence of Mary and her allies we drew ourselves up to our full height and said solemnly in unison, "We put the wart curse on you, Mary Mahoney." Then we stalked away.

We didn't believe for a moment in the wart curse, but we hoped Mary would. At first she was openly contemptuous, but to our delight, on the fourth evening she developed a horrible sty in her eye. We told everybody a sty was a kind of a wart and that we had Mary in our power. The next day Mary broke down and came around to our cabin and apologized in choked accents. She gave Eileen her best hair ribbon and me a little barrel that had a picture of Niagara Falls inside it, if you looked hard enough. We were satisfied.

Guinea Pig

MY FRIGHTFUL EXPERIENCES WITH THE
RED CROSS.

Guinea Pig

I WAS nearly drowned, in my youth, by a Red Cross Lifesaving Examiner, and I once suffered, in the noble cause of saving human life from a watery grave, a black eye which was a perfect daisy and embarrassed me for days. Looking back on my agonies, I feel that none of my sacrifices, especially the black eye, were in the least worth while. Indeed, to be brutally frank about it, I feel that the whole modern school of scientific lifesaving is a lot of hogwash.

Of course, I've had rather bad luck with lifesavers, right from the beginning. Long before I ever had any dealings with professional lifesavers my sister nearly drowned me, quite by mistake. My father once took us to a northern Michigan fishing camp, where we found the life very dull. He used to go trolling for bass on our little lake all day long, and at night come home to our lodge, dead-beat and minus any bass. In the meantime Eileen and I, who were nine and ten at the time, used to take an old rowboat out to a shallow section of the lake and, sitting in the hot sun, feed worms to an unexciting variety of small, undernourished fish called gillies. We hated the whole business.

Father, however, loved to fish, even if he didn't catch a single fish in three weeks, which on this trip he didn't. One night, however, he carried his enthusiasm beyond a decent pitch. He decided to go bass fishing after dark, and rather than leave us alone in the lodge and up to God knows what, he ordered us to take our boat and row along after him.

Eileen and I were very bored rowing around in the dark, and finally, in desperation, we began to stand up and rock the boat, which resulted, at last, in my falling into the lake with a mighty splash.

When I came up, choking and mad as anything, Eileen saw me struggling, and, as she always says with a catch in her voice, she only meant to help me. Good intentions, however, are of little importance in a situation like that. For she grabbed an oar out of the lock, and with an uncertain gesture hit me square on the chin.

I went down with a howl of pain. Eileen, who could not see much in the darkness, was now really frightened. The cold water revived me after the blow and I came to the surface, considerably weakened but still able to swim over to the boat. Whereupon Eileen, in a noble attempt to give me the oar to grab, raised it once again, and socked me square on the top of the head. I went down again, this time without a murmur, and my last thought was a vague wonder that my own sister should want to murder me with a rowboat oar.

As for Eileen, she heard the dull impact of the oar on my head and saw the shadowy figure of her sister disappear. So she jumped in the lake, screeching furiously, and began to flail around in the water, howling for help and looking for me. At this point I came to the surface and swam over to the boat, with the intention of killing Eileen.

Father, rowing hard, arrived just in time to pull us both out of the water and prevent me from attacking Eileen with the rowboat anchor. The worst part about the whole thing, as far as I was concerned, was that Eileen was considered a heroine and Father told everybody in the lake community that she had saved my life. The postmaster put her name in for a medal.

After what I suffered from amateur lifesaving, I should have known enough to avoid even the merest contact with the professional variety of water mercy. I learned too late that being socked with an oar is as nothing compared to what the Red Cross can think up.

From the very beginning of that awful lifesaving course I took the last season I went to a girls' camp, I was a marked woman. The rest of the embryo lifesavers were little, slender maidens, but I am a peasant type, and I was monstrously big for my fourteen years. I approximated, in poundage anyway, the theoretical adult we energetic young lifesavers were scheduled to rescue, and so I was, for the teacher's purpose, the perfect guinea pig.

The first few days of the course were unpleasant for me, but not terribly dangerous. The elementary lifesaving hold, in case you haven't seen some hapless victim being rescued by our brave beach guardians, is a snakelike arrangement for supporting the drowning citizen with one hand while you paddle him in to shore with the other. You are supposed to wrap your arm around his neck and shoulders, and keep his head well above water by resting it on your collarbone.

This is all very well in theory, of course, but the trick that none of Miss Folgil's little pupils could master was keeping the victim's nose and mouth above the waterline. Time and again I was held in a viselike grip by one of the earnest students with my whole face an inch or two under the billowing waves.

"No, no, Betsy," Miss Folgil would scream through her megaphone, as I felt the water rush into my lungs. "No, no, you must keep the head a little higher." At this point I would begin to kick and struggle, and generally the pupil would have to let go while I came up for air. Miss Folgil was always very stern with me.

"Ruth," she would shriek from her boat, "I insist! You must allow Betsy to tow you all the way in. We come to Struggling in Lesson Six."

This was but the mere beginning, however. A few lessons later we came to the section of the course where we learned how to undress under water in forty seconds. Perhaps I should say we came to the point where the *rest* of the pupils learned how to get rid of shoes and such while holding their breaths. I never did.

There was quite a little ceremony connected with this part of the course. Miss Folgil, and some lucky creature named as timekeeper and armed with a stop-watch, rowed the prospective victim out to deep water. The pupil, dressed in high, laced tennis shoes, long stockings, heavy bloomers, and a middy blouse, then stood poised at the end of the boat. When the timekeeper yelled "Go!" the future boon to mankind dived into the water and, while holding her breath under the surface, unlaced her shoes and stripped down to her bathing suit. Miss Folgil never ex-

53

plained what connection, if any, this curious rite had with saving human lives.

I had no middy of my own, so I borrowed one of my sister's. My sister was a slender little thing and I was, as I said, robust, which puts it politely. Eileen had some trouble wedging me into that middy, and once in it I looked like a stuffed sausage. It never occurred to me how hard it was going to be to get that middy off, especially when it was wet and slippery.

As we rowed out for my ordeal by undressing, Miss Folgil was snappish and bored.

"Hurry up," she said, looking irritated. "Let's get this over with quick. I don't think you're ready to pass the test, anyway."

I was good and mad when I jumped off the boat, and determined to Make Good and show that old Miss Folgil, whom I was beginning to dislike thoroughly. As soon as I was under water, I got my shoes off, and I had no trouble with the bloomers or stockings. I was just beginning to run out of breath when I held up my arms and started to pull off the middy.

Now, the middy, in the event you don't understand the principle of this girl-child garment, is made with a small head opening, long sleeves, and no front

54

opening. You pull it on and off over your head. You do if you are lucky, that is. I got the middy just past my neck so that my face was covered with heavy linen cloth, when it stuck.

I pulled frantically and my lungs started to burst. Finally I thought the hell with the test, the hell with saving other people's lives, anyway. I came to the surface, a curious sight, my head enfolded in a water-soaked middy blouse. I made a brief sound, a desperate glub-glub, a call for help. My arms were stuck in the middy and I couldn't swim. I went down. I breathed in large quantities of water and linen cloth.

I came up again, making final frantic appeals. Four feet away sat a professional lifesaver, paying absolutely no attention to somebody drowning right under her nose. I went down again, struggling with last panic-stricken feverishness, fighting water and a middy blouse for my life. At this point the time-keeper pointed out to Miss Folgil that I had been under water for eighty-five seconds, which was quite a time for anybody. Miss Folgil was very annoyed, as she hated to get her bathing suit wet, but, a thoughtful teacher, she picked up her megaphone, shouted to the rest of the class on the beach to watch, and dived in after me.

If I say so myself, I gave her quite a time rescuing me. I presented a new and different problem, and probably am written up in textbooks now under the heading "What to Do When the Victim Is Entangled in a Tight Middy Blouse." Miss Folgil finally towed my still-breathing body over to the boat, reached for her bowie knife, which she carried on a ring with her whistle, and cut Eileen's middy straight up the front. Then she towed me with Hold No. 2 right in to the shore and delivered me up to the class for artificial respiration. I will never forgive the Red Cross for that terrible trip through the water, when I might have been hoisted into the boat and rowed in except for Miss Folgil's overdeveloped sense of drama and pedagogy.

I tried to quit the lifesaving class after that, but the head councilor at the camp said I must keep on, to show that I was the kind of girl who always finished what she planned to do. Otherwise, she assured me, I would be a weak character and never amount to anything when I grew up.

So I stayed for Lesson 6: "Struggling." After that I didn't care if I never amounted to anything when I grew up. In fact, I hoped I wouldn't. It would serve everybody right, especially Miss Folgil. I came

a little late to the class session that day and missed
the discussion of theory, always held on the beach
before the actual practice in the lake. That was just
my hard luck. I was always a child of misfortune.
I wonder that I survived my youth at all.

"We were waiting for you, Ruth," Miss Folgil
chirped cheerily to me as I arrived, sullen and downcast, at the little group of earnest students sitting on
the sand.

"What for?" I said warily. I was determined not
to be a guinea pig any more. The last wave had
washed over my helpless face.

"You swim out," Miss Folgil went on, ignoring
my bad temper, "until you are in deep water—about
twelve feet will do. Then you begin to flail around
and shout for help. One of the students will swim
out to you."

All of this sounded familiar and terrible. I had
been doing that for days, and getting water in my
nose for my pains.

"But when the student arrives," Miss Folgil went
on, "you must not allow her to simply tow you away.
You must struggle, just as hard as you can. You must
try to clutch her by the head, you must try to twine

57

your legs about her, and otherwise hamper her in trying to save you."

Now, *this* sounded something like. I was foolishly fired by the attractive thought of getting back at some of the fiends who had been ducking me in the name of science for the past two weeks. Unfortunately, I hadn't studied Chapter 9, entitled "How to Break Holds the Drowning Swimmer Uses." Worse, I hadn't heard Miss Folgil's lecture on "Be Firm with the Panic-Stricken Swimmer—Better a Few Bruises Than a Watery Grave." This last was Miss Folgil's own opinion, of course.

So I swam out to my doom, happy as a lark. Maybelle Anne Pettijohn, a tall, lean girl who ordinarily wore horn-rimmed spectacles, was Miss Folgil's choice to rescue Exhibit A, the panic-stricken swimmer.

I laughed when I saw her coming. I thought I could clean up Maybelle Anne easily enough, but alas, I hadn't counted on Maybelle Anne's methodical approach to life. She had read Chapter 9 in our textbook, and she had listened carefully to Miss Folgil's inspiring words. Besides, Maybelle Anne was just naturally the kind of girl who ran around doing people dirty for their own good. "This may hurt your feelings," she used to say mournfully, "but I feel I have to tell you . . ."

When Maybelle Anne got near me, I enthusiastically lunged for her neck and hung on with both hands while getting her around her waist with my legs. Maybelle Anne thereupon dug her fingernails into my hands with ferocious force, and I let go and swam away, hurt and surprised. This was distinctly not playing fair.

"What's the idea?" I called out.

"It says to do that in the book," Maybelle Anne replied, treading water.

"Well, you lay off of that stuff," I said, angered, book or no book. Maybelle Anne was a Girl Scout, too, and I was shocked to think she'd go around using her fingernails in a fair fight.

"Come on, struggle," Maybelle Anne said, getting winded from treading water. I swam over, pretty reluctant and much more wary. Believe it or not, this time Maybelle Anne, who was two medals from being a Beaver or whatever it is Girl Scouts with a lot of medals get to be, bit me.

In addition to biting me, Maybelle Anne swung her arm around my neck, with the intention of towing me in to the shore. But I still had plenty of fight

59

left and I had never been so mad in my life. I got Maybelle Anne under water two or three times, and I almost thought I had her when suddenly, to my earnest surprise, she hauled off and hit me as hard as she could, right in the eye. Then she towed me in, triumphant as anything.

Maybelle Anne afterward claimed it was all in the book, and she wouldn't even apologize for my black eye. Eileen and I fixed her, though. We put a little garter snake in her bed and scared the daylights out of her. Maybelle Anne was easy to scare anyway, and really a very disagreeable girl. I used to hope that she would come to a bad end, which, from my point of view, at least, she did. Maybelle Anne grew up to be a Regional Red Cross Lifesaving examiner.

I'll bet she just loves her work.

Noel Coward and Mrs. Griffin

OUR DISMAL ATTEMPTS TO GET CULTURED
AND HOW MR. COWARD RUINED OUR LIVES,

MY sister and I had a lot of trouble in our youth trying to get cultured. Every time we made a small attempt to explore science, religion, or the fine arts, public opinion was against us. In the end, Noel Coward blasted our reputations and in the opinion of our fond family, ruined our lives once and for all.

Of course, Noel Coward was only the climax. Before Noel Coward, Eileen and I got mixed up in a scandal about Michael Arlen, not to mention the time Father actually called in the pastor of the East Cleveland Evangelical Church to remonstrate with Eileen because she buried her doll on Good Friday and expected it, or said she expected it (no one ever knew the real truth of the matter), to resurrect itself on Easter.

That doll business caused a terrible uproar in the family. Of course, I admit it was a little thoughtless of Eileen to let the neighbors in on the big experi- ment. Inquiring minds, ought, I suppose, to operate only in the bosom of the family.

At least that was Father's position. He was cer- tainly furious when Mrs. Griffin, a lady who was strongly pro bono publico, came rushing into the kitchen the night before Easter.

"Mr. McKenney," Mrs. Griffin bleated, sidestepping great pools of Easter egg dye, "do you KNOW that your little girl Eileen has been COMMITTING SACRILEGE?"

"Uhmmm?" Father murmured. He was engrossed in dying a hard-boiled egg half blue and half red, an operation which he had boasted he could do blindfolded, it was that easy. Eileen and I were watching his pitiful attempts with the contempt they merited. He had already spoiled four eggs.

"Bobbie came home tonight and wanted to borrow Sue's doll. He said he wanted to crucify it and hurry up and bury it so that it could Rise tomorrow." Mrs. Griffin's outraged squeal echoed in our quiet kitchen. Eileen looked up from her work, and an expression of gentle modesty, of unassuming pride, flickered in her large blue eyes.

"He did, huh?" Father remarked pleasantly, and added as an afterthought, "Tsk! Tsk!"

"Why, MR. MC KENNEY!" Mrs. Griffin's howl rang out at the same instant that Father's egg slipped from his spoon and fell into the kettle of red dye.

"God damn it to hell!" Father said. Eileen and I turned our heads so that he should not see our complacent smiles. It does not pay, we early learned, to gloat over the misfortunes, however merited, of one's parents.

"Why, Mr. McKenney," Mrs. Griffin repeated in a dying swan voice. You could see she was pretty shaken.

Father wheeled, the spoon, still dripping red dye, in his hand. "What do you want?" he screamed. Father had been trying to dye that egg two colors for more than an hour. He was a man who could never let a dare alone.

"Really! Mr. McKenney!"

"Well," said Father, gradually pulling himself together. He put down his spoon, very carefully, glanced murderously at his two daughters and led Mrs. Griffin into the living room.

"Bobbie Griffin," Eileen murmured, as the lad's mother disappeared around the door, "is a rat."

She was right. Ten minutes later, Bobbie, armed with a flashlight and goaded by his mother, pointed out the very spot where Eileen's doll, Joe, renamed for the big experiment, had been carefully buried in our backyard. Father dug Joe up with a hand trowel at a little after ten o'clock that night, in spite of Eileen's tearful complaints. "He'll Rise tomorrow and you won't have to trouble," Eileen kept moaning.

Mrs. Griffin and Father were of two minds about the whole situation. Mrs. Griffin said Eileen really didn't believe Joe would Rise, she was just trying to ruin the faith of Mrs. Griffin's angel-child Bobbie.

"Eileen!" Father intoned sternly, "if you were really trying to prove to Bobbie that Joe couldn't and wouldn't Rise, you are a bad little girl and need punishing, but if you were only a little confused about Easter I will have Dr. Ringing come to talk to you."

Eileen chose Dr. Ringing. She has been a realist from her tenderest years.

We lost interest in religion after the Easter fiasco and turned, rather suddenly, to Michael Arlen. Eileen and I have always believed that Michael Arlen was Father's fault, and we considered his behavior when the matter came, somewhat unfortunately, to public light, both unjust and extravagant. For Father, in the interests of teaching his twelve- and thirteen-year-old daughters the value of a penny, got us jobs minding infants while their parents were over playing bridge with the adult McKenneys.

It was a nice arrangement. Father was quite some

66

bridge player and even at a tenth of a cent a point it was a dull evening when he couldn't collect a week's cigar money from his guests. In the meantime, his daughters, little business women that they were, were stripping the neighbors' shelves of all loose chocolate candy, peanuts, and other edibles and presumably listening for the night wails, if any, of scores of disagreeable little children, at $1.25 a night.

We were a little sullen about our work at first, since it was billed as a big character-building project and we had to put all our profits in the bank, but one night, while close on the scent of a box of chocolate candy we felt sure Mrs. Envry had hidden somewhere in her large house, we came across Michael Arlen. Mr. Arlen was hidden behind a volume of the collected works of Harold Bell Wright, on the Envry bookshelves. The Envrys lived across the street and had a mighty-lunged child named Little Cartwright. Big Cartwright was Mr. Envry. He wore glasses and sold insurance, although not to Father.

Eileen and I began to take a real interest in our work after we started reading *The Green Hat*. In fact, we couldn't wait to get back to the Envrys to see what happened next to poor, brave Iris March and her fascinating wonderful friends. Father got quite smug about us. He said we reminded him of himself when he was a little lad and sold newspapers at three o'clock on cold winter mornings.

"When was that, Father," Eileen asked once, "when you lived on that farm and milked the cows just as dawn came up over the snowy hills?" Eileen was always making Father mad.

Lenora MacAbee's mother, a somewhat hysterical lady who used to imagine her house was burning down twice every winter, broke the Michael Arlen scandal. She stuck her head in Lenora's little back-yard playhouse just as I was assigning the parts in our big homemade drama, "The Green Hat."

"You," I was ordering Lenora, "are Iris' boy friend, and I am her husband, and Eileen gets to be Iris, but tomorrow I'm going to be."

"Eeeek!" Mrs. MacAbee said, calling our attention to her undesired presence.

It developed that Mrs. MacAbee was a woman of the world, at least on East Cleveland, Ohio, standards. She instantly recognized the name "Iris" which was more than Father did. When Mrs. MacAbee appeared dramatically in our living room, dragging Eileen and me behind her, she ran into something of an anti-climax. Father had to be told who Iris March

68

was, and who Michael Arlen was, and finally Mrs. MacAbee had to ask us to leave the room while she explained to the innocent Mr. McKenney just what was wrong with both Mr. Arlen and Iris. Father was never a great one for literary sensations.

Eileen and I and Mrs. Envry took the whole thing very hard. Mrs. Envry moved, taking along her Cartwrights, Big and Little, and Eileen kept saying stubbornly to any and all adults who would listen to her, "But WHY was Iris a bad lady?"

Father was never sure whether Eileen was just asking to be mean or whether she really didn't know. Mrs. Griffin said Eileen knew all right. Mrs. Griffin took rather a somber view of the general Michael Arlen situation. She said we were ruined for life and when Father somewhat uneasily demurred, Mrs. Griffin just said tartly, "You mark my words, they'll go from bad to worse."

Father didn't believe it at the time, but I guess he came around to Mrs. Griffin's point of view when we got embroiled in the Noel Coward incident a year or so later.

Surprising as it may seem, Noel Coward happened to us because our sextette of doting aunts on the Farrel side of the family thought we should sit at the feet of Shakespeare and quit going to those horrid movies all the time.

We were big girls, Aunt Molly said, already thirteen and fourteen years old, and it was about time we got some culture in our lives. She organized a sort of combine among the Farrel aunts. Every Saturday afternoon a different aunt bought us fifty-cent matinée tickets for the Ohio Theater, and every Saturday afternoon we got dressed in our best, hunted up our gloves and our handkerchiefs and trotted off, accompanied by a somewhat bored Farrel aunt to see Robert Mantell bang around the stage in "Macbeth," or Walter Hampden recite, "Love, I love beyond breath, beyond reason," etc.

It was our first season at the theatre and we had a wonderful time. We admired Mr. Mantell extravagantly and were very indignant when Aunt Kate said, during the intermission, that she didn't know if she could sit through another act, he was better forty years before.

Then came the great Saturday when Aunt Molly had a cold and we went by ourselves to see Ethel Barrymore in "The Second Mrs. Tangueray." Miss Barrymore was, we thought, simply wonderful and the play was so wonderfully sad, especially where she killed herself, and we ate three chocolate bars in the intermission and altogether it was a wonderful Saturday afternoon.

The rest of the aunts immediately developed permanent Saturday afternoon colds and soon we got accustomed to trotting off to the matinées unchaperoned. Aunt Molly just went down to the box office at the Ohio Theater and ordered two fifty-cent matinée tickets for the rest of the season. The Ohio Theater had a new play every week, for in those days Cleveland got all the New York shows a season late. All that glorious winter Eileen and I throbbed to the drama with real people in it, which we much preferred even to Lon Chaney movies.

Every now and then we sat through some mighty mystifying plays on our Saturday excursions. We didn't mind obscurity, however; we rather liked it. We even thought Ibsen was fine because the costumes were so quaint and everybody seemed to be having such awfully sad times and all the characters had their lives ruined by something or other. The Saturday we saw "The Captive," a nasty old woman, a perfect stranger, walked right up to us in the lobby after Act II and said she didn't know what our parents, if any, were thinking of. This immediately revived our interest in what had seemed a very dull show.

Noel Coward didn't seem dull, however, even if "The Vortex" was one of the most mysterious dramas of the season, as far as we were concerned. Mr. Coward was very satisfying. He was constantly ripping around the stage talking about his ruined life and playing like mad on a big piano. He ran his fingers through his hair quite a lot, too, and appeared to be constantly, from the very beginning of Act I, on the verge of suicide.

Father was rather impatient with our idle prattle that night. We tried to tell him at dinner about Noel Coward and how sad the play had been but he said for Heaven's sake to stop talking all the time, we were driving him crazy, he had worries.

Poor Father, he developed a whole new set of worries when Mrs. Griffin came over to play bridge the next Tuesday night. She bustled into our house exuding virtue at every pore. Eileen and I retreated upstairs after sullenly shaking her dry wrinkled hand. We were engaged in pouring some of Father's eau de cologne over our hair brushes so that we would be beautiful like the tragic Irene Soames in Mr. Galsworthy's great epic, when we heard Mrs.

Griffin's strident voice raised in excited conversation.

"And I said to Mr. Griffin, didn't I, Griffie, when I got home, I never knew such things were going on in the world."

We heard Father say, "Uhm" and then, "four hearts."

"Honestly, it was the first time I had been to the theatre since I was a girl and Mother took me to see little Eva, and if this is the kind of thing that's been going on in the theatre lately, I say, burn down the theatres."

"Double," Mr. Griffin said in his birdlike voice.

"Four spades, and really, I saw young girls in that audience. At least they ought to keep young girls away from that sort of filth."

"I'm sorry," Father replied pleasantly, as he put down his cards. "I haven't any spades. What was the play?"

"No spades! Well! Really, Mr. McKenney! Oh, the play was something called 'The Vortex' and there was a man called Howard or Coward I guess it was who wrote it and acted in it, too."

"Double trouble," Eileen said somberly, upstairs.

Downstairs we heard Father scrape his chair. He was getting to his feet. "Just what was the matter

73

with the play, Mrs. Griffin?" His voice sounded pretty somber.

"The play?" Mrs. Griffin squeaked.

"I SAID WHAT WAS WRONG WITH THIS HOWARD OR COWARD OR WHATEVER YOU CALL HIM?"

"Why, Mr. McKenney!" Mrs. Griffin's bleat was tremolo. "I don't know what gets into you, shouting like that."

"Now listen, Mrs. Griffin." Father's voice was back down to sub-basement levels, although slightly shaky. "Just tell me as simply as you can why you do not consider this Howard or Coward or whoever he was fit for Eileen and Ruth to see."

"Eileen and Ruth!" Mrs. Griffin sounded pleased. "Mercy! Don't tell me they saw that awful business!"

"MRS. GRIFFIN," Father thundered, "PLEASE."

"Well, in the play, he was in love with his mother."

Father was gruff. "Go ahead."

"Well, that was it."

"WHAT WAS IT?" Father howled. Eileen and I were right with him there, all agog. But while we waited with baited breath to hear the worst, we were

74

surprised to mark the sound of Father sinking into his chair and muttering, "My GOD."

"Isn't it terrible?" Mrs. Griffin twittered enthusiastically.

It *was* pretty terrible. Mrs. Griffin said she thought Father ought to send us to a convent or to a reform school, or somewhere. Eventually we were called downstairs and in the uproar Father shouted, "And you are never going to the theatre again until you are grown up and I can't stop you."

"Father!" Eileen wept, "PLEASE let us go just this next week."

"Please," I screeched through my tears.

"Well," Father muttered, weakening under the deluge of his daughters' watery grief, "what's coming next week you want to see so much?"

Eileen sniffled, blew her nose, and feeling that all was not yet lost, said hopefully, " 'What Price Glory.' "

Mrs. Griffin said that was the last straw. She said that *showed* you what Noel Coward could do.

Chickie Has a Baby

MY sister and I have been addicts of the newspaper serial ever since we learned about babies from a thrilling tale called *Chickie*, by Elenore Meherin, published in daily installments by a Cleveland newspaper back in the early nineteen-twenties. I feel that nothing can help us, that no cure is drastic enough to save us now. I had hoped that as advancing years put the first streak of gray on our temples, we would lose interest in whether or not the latest heroine is besmirched at the hands of the latest villain, but such, unfortunately, has not been the case.

God knows, we have attempted to conquer our passion for newspaper serials. Once, not long ago, when I was trying to break away from the outpourings of Mr. Rob Eden, the author of the serial I am now following, I read for ten days no other paper than the *Times*, which, no doubt as a favor to readers like me, does not publish Mr. Eden's works. But the only result was that I took to dreaming about Augur, who sends to the *Times* those stimulating dispatches on European politics. I dreamed that Augur looked like a big black snake with a monocle, spats, and a Homburg hat. After I had dreamed about this for several nights, I quietly rejoined Eileen in her dismal devotion to Mr. Eden.

Mr. Eden, in the happy event that you are not

familiar with his work, is an enormously prolific and stupendously widely read author of lush love stories. His masterpieces are published in daily installments by newspapers all over the country. Millions hang on his merest exclamation point and throb to his familiar situations. Including Eileen and me.

I feel, taking my own and Eileen's terrifying cases as an example, that a newspaper-serial addict is practically born that way, or at least falls prey to the ugly disease early in childhood. I have an acquaintance, it is true, who was brought up very carefully as a reader of the New York *Sun*, and who then, late in life, ventured into Pennsylvania, where she came face to face with her first Rob Eden serial, in one of the Philadelphia papers. Now she can't let the man's work alone. Although she lives in New York, on Twelfth Street, near Fifth Avenue, she subscribes to the Philadelphia paper just to see what's what in the world of virtue triumphant and sin abashed. I consider that she's pretty far gone, but not as far gone as Eileen and I are.

The works of Mr. Rob Eden are tame if you put them alongside the story called *Chickie*, which we read when we were not old enough to know better than to get mixed up with a newspaper serial. We have to go along with Mr. Eden's serials now because we can find nothing stronger. *Chickie* was a classic story of a flapper who went bad. I hasten to add that this flapper reformed in the end and got married, and that anyway she sinned only because the villain took advantage of her innocence. But she sinned; and when we read *Chickie*, we were innocent, merry, prattling lasses of nine and ten.

Chickie, if not the first, at least the most sensational newspaper serial ever published, was printed in Cleveland by the *Press*, a Scripps-Howard newspaper (Give Light, and the People Will Find Their Own Way). I have always held *Chickie* against the *Press* because otherwise the *Press* was (and is) quite a good newspaper.

Chickie made a perfectly enormous sensation in Cleveland. Ministers, quivering with rage, denounced it from the pulpit. Schoolteachers told their pupils it was vulgar and immoral. Mothers tried to prevent their little ones from even peeping at the unchaste columns of the *Press*. And everyone, of course, read it feverishly. In the circle in which Eileen and I moved in those days, people read it mostly in secret.

During those stirring times, when each new day brought a new thrill and people could hardly wait for the paper boy to bang the *Press* up on the front porch, we once caught my poor Aunt Molly, red-handed, eagerly drinking down the fresh installment of *Chickie*. Aunt Molly, who claimed that her favorite author was the late Mr. Galsworthy, was considered very high-toned by the rest of the family. When we ran across her hiding behind the kitchen stove with her copy of the *Press*, she bought our silence with new dimes and a promise of two ice-cream cones. That incident undid all the lessons we had learned at the East Cleveland Evangelical Church School and taught us that duplicity exists even among the pure of heart.

As a matter of fact, *Chickie* differed in two or three rather important aspects from any other newspaper serial ever published since. In the first place, it included a famous seduction scene, in which the heroine really was seduced. Now, in Mr. Eden's seduction scenes (and he always has at least one, and sometimes several, in each masterpiece), the heroine invariably escapes her horrid fate. Chickie, however, did not.

That seduction scene in *Chickie* made such an impression on our youthful minds that we have never forgotten it. The villain in this sad tale hired a canoe or rowboat or sailboat—these little details escape me now, after all these years. Anyway, he transported our Chickie to an island. She was a fresh young flapper and she wore short skirts and lipstick, but she was really a good girl at heart. At least she was a good girl until he got her to the island. I remember this island well. It was quite a small island and very isolated. Chickie ran furiously around it several times, hallooing for help, and of course in vain.

Do not get the idea, however, that Chickie's virtue was overcome by brute force. The seduction lasted through several installments, and on Thursday and Friday it looked as though the black-hearted dog in the story was risking a criminal-assault charge. But on Saturday, Monday, and Tuesday, he changed his tactics. He said that he loved her.

Alas, the brute lied! Chickie was a pretty silly, foolish little flapper, with hardly a brain to call her own, but she had the stamina to resist all through Thursday, Friday, Saturday, and Monday. On Tuesday, however, the moon had come up, a soft breeze was stirring, her breath had begun to come in short gasps, and some trees on the island were whispering, "You love him, you love him." The villain clinched the thing by bringing in a religious angle. He called on God to witness his pure intentions, and that got her.

It also got most of Cleveland, even our aunts, whose moral code was strict and stern, but who couldn't help feeling sorry for poor Chickie, the innocent victim of that moonlight and those talking trees.

Immediately after the big seduction, everything in Chickie's life went to hell, fast. Her fine old father got sick and almost died. Her lover turned out to be a beast and, of course, deserted her. I think he married a rich girl, but I'm not sure. Anyway, he ran away from the inevitable results of his criminal passion.

For—and all of Cleveland held its breath at this daring passage in the story—Chickie had a baby. The installment in which Chickie discovered her horrid condition was nearly as famous, in northern Ohio, as the big seduction scene. Eileen and I read it together with popping eyes, and it set back our knowledge of the world by at least four years.

Chickie, who was, apparently, as dumb as she was pure, had been nursing her old father for months, never giving a thought to elementary biology. One day, after Papa was on the road to recovery, she slipped into a skirt and sweater and took a gander at herself in the mirror. From there on, the installment was breathless. She looked and looked. And then again. A slow flush mounted to her beautiful cheek. Tears came to her eyes. She wiped them off her hot cheeks to get another look in the mirror. Then she fell on her bed, sobbing. (Continued in tomorrow's Cleveland *Press*.)

You can imagine where this left us. We felt for Chickie and her sobs, but it was curiosity that really consumed us. What was wrong with poor Chickie? Why did she look in the mirror and fall on her bed sobbing? What was up, anyway? We moped around for two solid hours, turning the problem over in our fevered minds. Then we overheard Aunt Molly telling our uncle, who didn't read *Chickie*, and was a perfect brute about it, too, "Just imagine, John! Poor Chickie is going to have a baby."

My uncle said rudely, "I think you are losing your mind," but we didn't listen to his unfeeling remarks about people who read *Chickie*. We crept away, scared to death. For days I braided my pigtails, washed my face, and put on my middy blouses without a glance in my bedroom mirror. Eileen's natural interest in her curly hair disappeared. Finally I forgot and looked one day, and nothing happened, so we got over our panic. But it certainly put a mark on us.

Everything turned out fine for Chickie in the end. We felt very relieved. She married that nice boy who had always faithfully loved her. She stopped using lipstick and settled down to be a good wife. She went through a lot, though, before she achieved that happy state of affairs, and we suffered with her.

Although *Chickie* was a huge success, the newspapers never dared again to publish a serial story so exciting. True, some of Mr. Eden's works of art skate on pretty thin ice, but I, at least, have never read another newspaper shocker where the unmarried heroine comes right out and has a baby. Times have changed and newspapers have taken a turn toward the discreet.

Mr. Eden, though, and his fellow-writers have evolved a really crafty technique of getting interesting without being immoral. In this new approach to sex, the story generally opens with a big wedding. The heroine, happy as a lark, comes trotting down the church aisle, blushing and grinning, and simply foaming with white satin and lace. The hero, however, is not the least bit happy. Sullen and furious, he stands waiting for his bride while the girl that he loves is either a bridesmaid or plays the organ.

You can see the possibilities in this ingenious plot. On his wedding night, the hero comes clean with the little woman and tells her he doesn't love her. In some stories he doesn't even like her; he hates her. In other tales, he thinks of her as a good friend. Anyway, he sleeps on the sofa in the bridal suite while the bewildered bride cries her little heart out in solitary sorrow, on the pillows of the big double bed.

The pair decide, however, to live in the same house or apartment, to keep up appearances. This is an important angle, and don't forget it. Here you have the hero roaming around the house thinking about the woman he loves, who is really just a mean old schemer, and the heroine brooding over her wedding silver and getting madder and madder. Finally, as the story goes along, the situation is reversed. The hero finds out that his dream girl is a no-good and falls in love with, of all people, his wife. Proximity does it, of course. But his wife by this time is very fed up with her dopey husband and will have none of him. That's what she says, although secretly, of course, she still loves him.

Now come the big passionate love scenes. The husband tries to seduce his wife, but it's all O.K. with the ministers in town, because, after all, the lovers are married. Sometimes the wife, influenced by the soft moonlight and the sound of a rippling stream, gives in right off. If she does, she's sorry, because the next morning she finds a letter to her husband from his old flame, and she doubts him for several installments. Sometimes she resists, like the cold, broken-hearted woman she is, and her husband, feeling he hasn't a chance, takes to drink and loses his job. It comes out all right in the end.

Now and then this plot is put into reverse. It's the girl who marries a man with whom she would rather just play tennis. Sometimes she even loathes her husband. This latter is a variation of the save-the-old-homestead idea. There is a lot of thin ice in this plot, however, and it is not very popular. The public these days does not like to read about a girl who is so depraved she would marry a man for his money and a good home.

However, the public does not mind in the least reading about a girl who almost marries a man for his money and is saved at the last moment by love. In fact, this is one of Eileen's favorite stories. She likes it best when love wins out at the very altar.

She told me about a perfectly dandy story I had missed where the heroine was so determined to marry for money that only an earthquake, which killed off the rich man, saved her.

There has never been a seduction scene in the newspapers that came up to the one in *Chickie*, of course, but from time to time Mr. Eden or his fellow-workers tear off a honey. I remember one beauty with a French hotel as the scene of the scheduled crime. Recent serial writers are always careful to put their seduction scenes in places where the hero can conveniently pop in, just in time, and ask what the hell is going on. This differs, you see, from the isolated-island background, where the girl hasn't a chance. The heroine in the French-hotel incident was a rich man's secretary who traveled around with him, sending telegrams and things. She was beautiful, extremely honest, and pure. The rich man, unlike most rich men who travel round with beautiful secretaries, was strikingly handsome, in an evil sort of way. He also had charm and personality. The hero was a newspaperman, a bit seedy and very poor, but with a strict code of morals.

Well, one night when the rich man had settled down for a bit of intensive work on the French

Riviera, he rings for his secretary. She comes in, shy as a dove, but actually madly in love with her boss. They talk a bit and the moonlight streams in the windows. Far off there is faint music. Suddenly the rich man whips a package out of his pocket. It is a jewel box. Inside lies a necklace of perfectly matched pearls. Wordlessly he slips the pearls around his secretary's neck and fastens the clasp. She touches the pearls with feverish hands.

"I want to kiss every pearl nestling now against your neck," whispers the plutocrat.

The secretary feels her senses reeling. She closes her eyes. The man who has too much money for his own good starts on his self-imposed marathon. The secretary feels her knees wobbling and her consciousness slipping. She fears she will faint, or worse. (Continued in tomorrow's Akron *Beacon Journal*.)

Next day, the rich man is still kissing every pearl. He has worked his way around to the hollow of his secretary's neck. The situation is unbearably tense. Suddenly there is a terrible knock at the door. The secretary starts.

"Pay no attention," the millionaire says in a throaty voice, casting all this pearl business to the winds and seizing his secretary in his strong, sinewy arms. The knocking keeps on, and finally the hero, having given fair warning, bursts into the room. Rich men, it appears, do not lock their doors, which is a good thing for honest secretaries.

This story had a rather novel end. The hero reproaches the rich man for his evil intentions, and the plutocrat repents, proving there is some good in bankers. However, the plutocrat is still in love with his secretary, and since he has promised not to seduce her, he marries her. The hero is best man at the wedding. Greater love hath no man.

Eileen and I thought that little tale was almost as good as *Chickie*. But not quite. Nobody had a baby.

Le Scandale International

ABOUT A LETTER A NASTY LITTLE FRENCH
BOY WROTE ME. BAD CESS TO HIM.

ONCE, while in the prime, not to say the first blush, of my early youth in Cleveland, Ohio, during those stirring days when I led the Shaw High School debating team from one intoxicating triumph to another, I was, I am still sorry to say, the cause and author of a fearful international scandal.

The whole disreputable mess had its roots in the deplorable fact that I was Shaw High School's champion debater, in spite of the fact that I stuttered. I was, in fact, a sort of local Demosthenes. "Take the Marines out of Nicaragua!" I used to thunder to a fairly spellbound audience. "Redeem America's g-g-good n-n-name."

I was a big success with my teachers and my doting family but, alas, a complete failure with my fellow-pupils. In fact, I was a moral leper, an outcast, among my contemporaries. Eileen shook her curly head over my career. No boy in his right mind would have been caught dead within ten miles of me. Girls regarded me with a kindly and patronizing charity.

"I don't see how you do it," Mary Tenor said one day in the washroom, as she put on a layer of forbidden lipstick. "You certainly are smart. I said to Johnnikins last night at the Mayfair—you know, Johnny German, only I call him Johnnikins—Ruth certainly is smart. . . ."

95

Johnny German was the handsomest boy in high school and played right end on the football team. The Mayfair was a Chinese dine-and-dance place much favored for an after-the-movies snack by the selecter few at Shaw High. I had never been there in my life. I would have cut off my right hand, the one I used to make my most telling gestures with, to have had the delirious pleasure of calling Johnny German "Johnnikins" at the Mayfair.

Of course, to be perfectly honest, I would never have been asked to the Mayfair by young Master German, even if I had not been a peerless public speaker. I took to Nicaragua as a last resort. For I was, in the first place, exactly two years and seven months younger than most of the maidens in my class. While they were bootlegging their first lipsticks and wangling high heels out of their doting mothers, I was still in the Growing Girl oxford stage. They had their hair marceled for parties, while mine hung in twin braids down the back of my disgusting middy blouse.

But it wasn't only my youth, it was my looks that marked me down as a social failure. After all, Eileen was a whole year younger than I was, and already she figured as the belle of the Epworth League and the sensation of the Eighth Grade. The bitter truth of the matter was that I was homely as a mud fence. I looked like exactly what I was, the ex-star of an all-boy (except me) baseball team and the current sensation of the Northern Ohio Debating League. I don't see how, looking back on that awful period of my life, I stood it at all.

I did, though. I endured my fourteenth year somehow, until suddenly one day a ray of sunlight came to brighten the sodden gloom of my despair.

The whole thing started in French class, of all places. I was simply terrible in French. Oh, I could read French well enough and I was a positive whizz at translating the French classics cut down to high-school size, but my teacher, Miss Parrish, used to tell me frankly that I had probably the worst French accent she had ever heard, even in Shaw High School, where French accents reached remarkable lows. Because of my stuttering, I could simply never learn how to say the most elementary French sentence. I sat in the back of the class, and Miss Parrish didn't even bother about me any more.

That particular day, though, I was reading a magazine hidden under my desk when Miss Parrish interrupted my wandering thoughts to announce,

"And, Ruth, your correspondent will be Alfonse Donater." I pricked up my ears. It appeared that all the boys and girls of the advanced-French class in Shaw High School were going to write letters to the pupils in an advanced-English class in some faraway *lycée* in France. Miss Parrish apologized to the young ladies among her students. She knew, she said, we would rather correspond with girls our own ages, but unfortunately the school with which she had made the arrangements for the hands-across-the-sea gesture had only boy pupils. Miss Parrish's girl students lowered their eyes, ready, apparently, to make the best of this disappointing situation. A few quiet giggles broke our brave silence.

Writing to strange young men in France sounded romantic, but at first it was just terribly dull. We had to write in French, in the first place, which severely handicapped dopes like Mary Tenor. Then our first few letters were regular school exercises. We had to write them in class, and have them corrected, and then copy them off in our best handwriting before we could ship them across the Atlantic.

Alfonse's first few letters seemed also to have been written under the eagle eyes of his teacher. Alfonse discussed in quaint but impeccable English the weather, the books he read, and his passionate desire to become a construction engineer and make a great deal of money. Alfonse sounded like a fearful prig to me. I began to lose interest. Then he sent me his picture. He was quite handsome.

Just after Alfonse's picture arrived, Miss Parrish announced that from now on correspondence with our dear little French friends was optional. She hoped we would continue writing to our faraway fellow-students and asked us kindly to be careful of our grammar.

I rushed home from school that night lugging a huge French dictionary and my French grammar. *"Cher Alfonse,"* I began. Shortly before midnight I wound up, *"Votre amie, Ruth."* In between these two phrases were three pages of the most dreadful lies I had ever told. I let Alfonse think I lived in a positive whirlwind of mad pleasure. I said his picture reminded me of my fourth best beau, who was on the football team.

"I will give you a picture of a day in my life," I wrote. *"Je vous donnerai un tableau de la jour dans ma vie [sic]."* My day, as I described it, was composed of a gay series of social events—a tea dance, a dinner engagement, a Junior Prom, and a bit of dancing at the Mayfair to wind it all up. One became, I said, rather bored with such a constant round of dances, but what could one do when one was so popular? I couldn't find a French word for that, so I finally compromised on *"bien-aimée,"* which sounded well, I thought.

I mailed this letter without a qualm and spent two dreamy weeks thinking about Alfonse. Then, really before I expected it, Alfonse's reply arrived, a pleasantly thick envelope studded with foreign stamps. I tore up the stairs, locked my bedroom door, opened the window, lit an absolutely forbidden cigarette, and settled down in comfort to read the letter from *mon cher* Alfonse. I tore open the flap. To my surprise, I found inside three closely written pages of French. Alfonse was supposed to write in English, the dope. I looked inside the envelope again. Perhaps there was a translation.

And so I saw the picture. It was a postcard-size affair, glossy and smooth. To the right was a lady whose style of hairdress indicated she had reached the prime of her youth in about 1910. She was clad in fluttering garments, cut much too low at the bosom, at least for my Puritan eyes. On the left was a gentleman with slick hair, clad in full evening dress, and reclining on one elegant knee. The photographer had caught the gentleman in the very act of passionately embracing the lady, who was, I supposed at first glance, his fiancée. Certainly there could be no other excuse for the way she was carrying on.

I regarded the picture with surprise. Perhaps this was Alfonse's none-too-delicate way of telling me he was engaged. I examined the figure of the gentleman with great care. No, I felt sure that this bemused stranger was not Alfonse. He looked too old and a touch too carefree to be a student at a respectable *lycée*.

Feeling slightly uneasy, I put the picture aside and took up the letter. Here I met complete defeat. Nothing I had ever learned in advanced French at Shaw High School helped in the least. All I could make out was the salutation, "Dear, dearest Ruth." This brought a faint blush and a further feeling of alarm. Alfonse seemed to be taking a lot for granted. I brooded over the French scrawl. Here and there I could make out a familiar word, such as *"l'amour."* The rest was lost in a deep obscurity. Victor Hugo (high-school-text edition) was never like this.

For days I burned with curiosity. If I had had any sense at all, I would have tossed Alfonse's pretty picture and Alfonse's mysterious billet-doux into the nearest wastepaper basket, but after all, this was the first letter from a boy I had ever received in my entire life—along personal lines, I mean—and I felt the outlook for getting another was none too bright.

I carried Alfonse's letter in my history book, and one day while the rest of Miss Teester's pupils were dully considering what General Grant said to General Lee, I trotted out the now somewhat worn pages and again tried to decipher my dear French fellow-student's fearful alien scrawl.

Lost in happy concentration, I did not, unfortunately, notice that Buster Lockmonton, who sat next to me, was also trying to make out Alfonse's handwriting. Buster Lockmonton was, in my opinion, the most revolting student at Shaw High School. In the first place, he was exactly my own age, a bare fifteen, while the rest of the boys in my class were seventeen going on eighteen. He was a disgusting child. He wore, for precisely the same reasons that I wore Growing Girl oxfords, knee pants. His very name, Buster, indicated his hopeless immaturity.

But young Master Lockmonton was not only young, he was rich, and nauseatingly proud of it. His parents had given dear Buster advantages. He had lived in France for four solid years, attending French schools. Miss Parrish said he spoke French better than some Frenchmen. He was constantly bringing souvenirs of his fascinating sojourn in France to school and every one of us at Shaw High had been liberally favored with Buster's memories of *la belle France*.

"Psssst," the horrid boy now signaled. I jumped and turned a slow but bright purple.

"Who's the letter from?" Buster muttered.

"None of your business," I replied.

"Buster!" Miss Teester warned.

Buster was momentarily reduced to silence, but his blood was up. The moment Miss Teester turned her back to write a few dates on the blackboard, Buster returned to his prey.

"It was in French," he whispered. "I can read French better than you can."

"Go fry an egg," I growled, but Buster had planted the germ of an idea in my harried mind.

All that evening during debating-team practice I toyed with the notion of letting Buster translate the letter. Could I trust him? Reason, instinct, and solid practical experience said no. Finally I decided that if Buster knew the Scout oath, I would make him swear eternal secrecy and have him copy out Alfonse's letter in English for me. I should have known better, of course, but by this time I was ready to throw reason to the winds.

Buster swore. He was so anxious to get hold of the letter that he rushed through the Scout oath, mumbling along at a rapid pace. I made him say it again slowly and I handed him the letter, complete with the picture, for I hoped there was an explanation somewhere in Alfonse's bad handwriting of my fellow-student's taste in art. Buster promised to give me a written translation in history class the next morning.

Mr. Lockmonton was nearly late for class that terrible day. He came in hurriedly and sat down without a word.

"Where is it?" I hissed as Miss Teester started off, "Good morning, class. Today we are to consider the closing Federal campaign in Georgia."

Buster pretended to be absorbed in Miss Teester's kittenish remarks about the origin of the song "Marching Through Georgia."

"Hand it over," I muttered.

"I can't," whispered Buster.

"You couldn't read it, then," I said, very nasty.

Buster shook his odious head. "I read it, but I can't tell you what's in it," he stage-whispered.

"Why not?" I demanded furiously, and lapsed into forced silence. Miss Teester was staring at me, full of reproach.

"Because," Buster growled when the danger was over, "it was too terrible. Boy, what was in that letter! And the picture! Wow!"

I began to feel very, very sick, and stared helplessly at Buster, appealing, I hoped, to his sense of chivalry. It was no use. Then the class bell rang.

"Hot diggety dog," Buster continued with enthusiasm, now that he could speak out loud. "Boy, you must have written that guy plenty!"

"I did not," I replied with dignity. "Give the letter back."

Buster handed the letter over. "And the picture," I snapped.

"I lost the picture by mistake," Buster answered blandly.

"You did not!" I cried hysterically. "Buster Lockmonton, if you have any Boy Scout honor, you will give that picture back!"

Buster scorned a reply. He walked out of the

room, murmuring, "What I know about Ruth, oh, boy, oh, boy, oh, boy!"

I went through the corridors of dear old Shaw High School for days in a kind of fevered sweat. Alfonse's letter, which I had reduced to ashes, could never be used as evidence against me, but the thought of Buster showing around that awful picture filled me with a shuddering horror.

It took Buster's Boy Scout honor rather longer to break down than I thought it would. Three days, to be exact. On the morning of the fourth day, Johnny German gave a long, low whistle as I walked into French class. I thought I would faint. I hoped I would faint. Nothing happened, though. I walked, my face purple red, to my desk. Mary Tenor immediately wrote me a note and slipped it over. "What I heard about you!" it read. From Buster to Johnny German to Mary Tenor to Miss Parrish was, I knew, a matter of days or even hours. I waited, the cold hand of death on my heart.

Miss Parrish was very brutal about it, I thought. "From now on," she announced in class a day or two later, "every letter written to France will first be brought to me for approval. I do not care to discuss the reason for this change in procedure. Ruth, will you see me after class, and also Buster Lockmon-ton?"

The class had minor convulsions. Johnny German whistled again. I waited to die of shame.

Miss Parrish began by making Buster produce the picture, after I said, with truth, that I had burned the letter. For a long time Buster and Miss Parrish and I stood in silence, regarding the gentleman in evening clothes embracing the lady in the low-cut fluttering garments.

"Well," Miss Parrish said at last. She tore the picture up with slow finality, made a neat pile of the scraps, and threw them carefully into her wastepaper basket. Buster and I watched this operation in heavy quiet.

"Now, Buster," she said, "you will please tell me, as nearly as you can remember, what was in that letter."

"I can't," Buster said desperately, "it's too terrible." A faint spot of color came to Miss Parrish's maiden cheek. I turned my ordinary high purple.

"Nevertheless, Buster," Miss Parrish said bravely, "I must know in order to report Alfonse to his teacher. No French boy can be allowed to insult a nice American girl, even on paper."

I wished passionately that I were dead, stone-dead, in a peaceful graveyard, where people would come and be sorry for me.

"Speak, Buster!" said Miss Parrish sharply.

"Miss Parrish," Buster cried in agony, "I don't know. I couldn't translate it. I just made up what I said." Then the insufferable boy burst into tears.

I have often wondered, in later years, now that I can bear to think about it, what was really in Alfonse's letter. After all, it *was* the first letter I ever got from a boy—of a personal nature, that is.

From Rags to Rags

WHY EILEEN AND I NEVER GOT ANYWHERE,
LIKE ANDREW CARNEGIE. ALSO WHAT
FATHER THOUGHT ABOUT IT.

EILEEN and I have always been very depressed by those engaging little tales of how captains of finance or editors of magazines or lady presidents of big important department stores made their mark in the world.

You know, the growing lad dashes out into the blistering wintah breeze to sell a mean newspaper. In about two months the head slugger in the circulation department recognizes true genius in the budding banker; he equips the ambitious boy with a Colt machine gun and from there on in our lion-hearted hero overcomes all obstacles including competitors and winds up complaining about labor unions to the president.

But Eileen and I are obviously never going to get anything from the Horatio Alger boys except sneers. I can't make out, alas, why we never got anywhere climbing up Life's Ladder. Here we are, with old age and retirement just around the corner, and nothing to show for years of blistering effort in the great Game of Life except a few sharp letters from the New York Telephone Company beginning, "Unless we receive by the 12th inst." Clearly we are stuck on the basement rungs of the Ladder noted above, and why?

After all, we started out by earning our first pennies selling newspapers. Or, well, to be a little more accurate, we earned our first motion-picture projector peddling subscriptions to a weekly ladies' magazine. The projector had a roll of film showing a man diving into a swimming pool and you could reverse the machine so that the athlete came out of the water and landed back on the springboard. It was quite funny that way.

The magazine was also slightly funny. It kept publishing *The Sheik* over and over again, in weekly installments. The whole family had three years' subscriptions (ninety cents for three years, big special offer) and everybody but Grandma Farrel got awfully sick of mad desert love and heaving passion under the moonlight. Grandma said she sort of missed *The Sheik* when, four years after we had tired of seeing the man come out of the water and go back on the springboard, the circulation department caught up with Grandma and cut her off the mailing list. Once, after the second year, Aunt Kate, who was a great one for getting her money's worth, wrote to ask when they were going to publish something else but patent medicine ads and *The Sheik*. She never got an answer.

After the motion-picture projector incident,

Eileen and I abandoned our careers as little business women for some months. Then we evolved a primitive but thriving barter system in milk bottles. We stole the household bottles which we traded in for candy at a delicatessen store around the corner. Eventually we talked the proprietor of the delicatessen store, which was named Bill's Poolroom, into giving us credit, and very shortly we were caught in an evil web of debt. We kept eating more and more Clark Bars, a delicious confection of the period, which in turn forced us to steal more and more milk bottles at an ever increasing rate. The gap between the number of milk bottles we could safely abscond with, and the number of Clark Bars we could and did eat grew larger and larger until at last we owed Bill's Poolroom seventy-four cents. The four cents was for a Clark Bar with its wrapper slightly torn which we were able to purchase at a bargain rate.

The proprietor of Bill's Poolroom, an evil character with floppy ears and little pig eyes, began to badger us. We were old hands at Dickens' novels and we began to fear the approaching shadow of a debtors' prison. We tried to sell the motion-picture projector but the bottom had fallen out of motion-picture projectors, even at sacrifice offers. I disposed

of four of my best hair ribbons and got the bill down
to fifty-three cents but then, encouraged by our apparent ability to pay, our crafty creditor let us go on
another Clark Bar orgy and finally we were faced
with the appalling total debt of eighty-two cents. At
this point the mean old proprietor of Bill's Poolroom
sent Father an itemized bill.

Father said he didn't know what we were coming
to. He said we certainly took after the Farrel side of
the family, all of which tribe threw their money
around like drunken sailors and ended up in their
old age dependent on the bounty of respectable characters like himself who did not squander their cash.
He said we would probably never amount to anything like John D. Rockefeller, Andrew Carnegie,
and Benjamin Franklin.

He brightened up a little, however, when I got a
job working nights in a print shop the summer I was
fourteen years old. The job was terribly exciting
because I was the center of a big ideological and
sociological struggle between the six night linotype
operators whom I passionately adored and Mr.
Heechum, aged seventy-four, the proofreader.

The linotype operators, who were all big handsome fellows and chewed tobacco expertly, scorned

Mr. Heechum because he was a veteran telephone-book proofreader whereas they were graduates of newspaper composing rooms. There is a big difference. Mr. Heechum, a true telephone-book type, was immediately convinced, the first night I set foot in the print shop to take over my combined duties of printer's devil, night elevator operator, and copy-holder, that the six linotype operators were out for no good as far as I was concerned.

This was a very surprising conclusion on Mr. Heechum's part, for I was not only a bare fourteen, still in ankle socks, hair ribbons, and braids, but I was also the homeliest girl in East Cleveland. The lino-type operators, who were all happily married, found Mr. Heechum's dark suspicions extremely hilarious. I thought they were flattering, and I used to blush up to my braids when Pete, the handsomest operator, would bellow out from his machine, "Hey! Sweet-heart! Light of my life! Pick up my galley pan and give me a nice big kiss!"

Mr. Heechum, who was a deacon in the Meth-odist Church and had a large nose like Cyrano's which constantly itched, causing him to scratch it with the lead end of his sharp proofreader's pencil, used to nearly have apoplexy when he heard Pete's fearful phrases. He would come dashing out of his proofroom, his pure white hair standing on end, his large floppy nose covered with pencil marks, waving galley proofs frantically and screeching, "You leave that girl alone, she's only fourteen years old."

Mr. Heechum had a great deal of trouble with me that summer, trying unsuccessfully to bring me up in the way a young girl should go. Pete and the rest of the linotype operators were belligerent Ingersoll atheists, enthusiastic Eugene Debs Socialists, old-time Wobblies, and passionate union men. Mr. Heechum, on the other hand, was not only godly and seventy-four, he was also a life-long Republican and he even used to stand up for Mr. J. P. Morgan during the hot arguments we all had as we sat around eating our 9 P.M. lunch. Pete said that showed you what a telephone-book printer was like.

As the summer wore along, a new crisis came to confront poor Mr. Heechum. Our shop was engaged in setting up in type, every night, the day's minutes of the 1927 Convention of the Brotherhood of Loco-motive Engineers. The convention was a very stormy one, for the delegates were in the day-to-day process of finding out their banks were busted, and their Florida island under water. The gentlemen who run the nation's trains were not the type who minced words. I used to sit beside dear old Mr. Heechum in our cubbyhole, reading along aloud, my voice professionally level. "Bro-ther Chair-man," I would chant in the copyholder's Chinese sing-song voice, "colon quote I rise to state that in my o-pin-ion these sons plural dash of dash . . ."

"You need a drink of water," Mr. Heechum used to say hastily, grabbing the copy out of my hands. I would obediently trot off to the water cooler and when I came back Mr. Heechum had safely read us past the infuriated remarks of the Brother from Wabash, Indiana. But five minutes later I would chant, "all cap I got to say is if any low down stink-i-n-g b-a-s . . ."

"Get a drink of water," Mr. Heechum would mutter hoarsely. Some nights I had a regular path worn to the water cooler by eleven o'clock, and it used to take me ages to pull galley proofs because naturally I had to read all the forbidden parts in type. Those engineers certainly had lush vocabularies when aroused. I got so I could read type like an old hand.

But Mr. Heechum finally gave me up when he discovered I gambled. I lost $2.25 in bets with Pete and some of the other operators on Jack Dempsey, and Mr. Heechum caught me paying off. Things were never the same between Mr. Heechum and myself. He said a man who gambled was bad enough but a fourteen-year-old girl, still in hair ribbons, who had the evil habit was past saving.

I guess I really was past saving at that, for Pete and his friends had made an indelible impression on my budding mind. Unlike the embryo banker who learns thrift and how to get ahead on his first job, all I ever learned was never to bet on an ex-champion's return bout, and what was wrong with the capitalistic system and God. None of these items ever got me very far in the great business world.

The summer I was sixteen something peculiar happened in Wall Street and the Cleveland job printing business collapsed with hardly time for a sigh. Father who was always a great reader of *The Saturday Evening Post* scoffed around the house for days. He said America was on its way up and nothing could stop it and it was unpatriotic of the printing business to collapse when everybody knew the most fabulous prosperity in the world was slated for the fall of 1929. Father's washing-machine business did not lie down and die until November, so he was extremely porky about my sudden unemployment. He said he had a feeling I was never going to be a success in life, always getting mixed up in queer industries that just sickened and blew up in smoke, poof!, when everybody else was making money hand over fist. He said he doubted if I would ever be able to support him in his old age. He said John D. Rockefeller never fooled around with the printing business, he was in oil up to his ears when but a lad.

John D. Rockefeller was never a waitress, either, but that was my next Port of Call in the great Cruise of Life. Father was always talking about the Cruise of Life, a nautical term he got from the night watchman at his factory. "I'm stuck at a way station on the Cruise of Life," Alex the watchdog used to tell Father. It made Father feel very badly. Here was poor Alex with eight children and only making $60 a month. Father mourned over Alex and his Cruise of Life until several years later Alex joined the union and got $76 a month. After that Father never mentioned the Cruise of Life. It made him mad just to think about that ungrateful Alex, biting the hand that had given him $60 a month all these years for just punching a few old time clocks and staying up all night. Indeed, adding insult to injury, Alex got to be what he called First Mate in his union and once pounded his fist right on Father's desk. Eileen said she thought Alex was repressed, he probably wanted to be a sailor in his youth. Father said no, he thought Alex just had a peculiar way of talking. Father was always so prosy.

It was Father in fact who made Eileen haul up the anchor and get in on the Life Cruising going on in our family. Father said, after I enlisted in the crew of the Harvey tearoom, that he couldn't see any reason why Eileen shouldn't earn an honest penny too. Eileen wept and said she was only fifteen and she was going to call up the juvenile court and get some justice around here. She said she didn't see why, if Father had two cars, of course the Maxwell was pretty old but it still ran, he had to put his youngest daughter out to work. She said she supposed he'd have her taking in washing next.

That made Father pretty mad. Did John D. Rockefeller charge $2.50 lipsticks to his Father? Did John D. Rockefeller take five of his little friends to his Father's golf club for lunch and run up a bill that would stagger Mr. J. P. Morgan? How in the name of God could five little high-school girls eat $17.80 worth of lunch? Wasn't it true that Eileen got the waiter to give her $10 in cash and put it on the bill so that she could buy a new tire for the Maxwell when she ran into a telephone pole and blew out the old one? Wasn't it?

Eileen said oh, all right, she didn't care, she'd just as soon be a waitress, they'd fire her anyway the first day because she stuttered. Father said that was the wrong attitude. He said just for that she couldn't go to Cape Cod in August with the Hunneckers (Billy Hunnecker, aged eighteen, was a simply gorgeous lad) unless she kept the waitress job right up to the week she was supposed to leave.

So Eileen was pretty chastened when she appeared at the Harvey employment office. Billy Hunnecker preyed on her mind and, besides, Father said she would have to buy her vacation clothes from the proceeds of her new job. Eileen had her eye on a one-piece white satin bathing suit that was currently priced at $17.50 in Cleveland's leading department store. Eileen had already tried it on and she said it fitted like a dream.

My sister even at the age of fifteen was East Cleveland's leading beauty and the Harvey people fell all over themselves hiring her. Good old Harvey's was opening a flock of new restaurants, lunch counters, soda fountains, and our tearoom in the recently completed Cleveland Union Station. The lunch rooms were supposed to get the grim, rude, traveling salesman trade, and the ladies who stood behind the curved counters were characters of mature years with plenty of experience in slapping down fresh customers.

The tearoom, on the other hand, was supposed to be Class: lunch eighty-five cents and one buck; tea from fifty cents up. We had a fountain with real fish and dripping vines, and people sat on red leather wall benches to gulp down our fancy food. Harvey's presumed that the fountain and the prices would keep the ordinary railroad-station trade out of our virginal haunts. We were banking on the suburban ladies who commuted in for a bit of shopping, and the management hired Eileen with no questions asked because she looked refined.

Opening day still frightens me in my dreams and Eileen claims it put a psychological mark on her. Eileen and I had never held a tray before in our lives, although Eileen was a great tennis player and a pretty good swan-diver. Since we had lied valiantly about our vast experience to get our jobs in the first place, nobody had seen fit to show us the little tricks professionals use to prevent customers receiving their lunches down their necks instead of on the table.

About 12:10 P.M. that fatal Monday, Eileen staggered out of the kitchen with four chicken patty lunches complete with Chef's Salad. She was even then a tall slender girl and pretty enough to get everybody's momentary attention. But Eileen got more than a passing glance from the cash customers that day. A solemn hush fell over the crowded tearoom as the clientele caught sight of my sister. Paunchy ladies half rose out of their red leather seats, napkins to their mouths to stifle little horrified screams.

For here was my suffering sister holding a huge burdened tray, not safely on the small of her arm, but straight out before her, at shoulder height. Her face was peony red. Her frilly lace cap was over her ear. Her eyes were glazed with horror. She had the gait of a tightrope walker. After each few steps she paused to stand trembling in her tracks, getting a fresh grip on her four chicken patty lunches. She progressed past crowded tables, and dignified old gentlemen ducked as the tray funeral-marched directly over their bald heads. The crowd began to murmur with horror. Obviously Eileen's slender arms were tiring under their burden. The tray rocked dangerously and a bit of Chef's Salad dripped on the hat of a paralyzed victim.

The hostess raced over, but Eileen shook her head. Apparently she felt she was past help. Her face turned redder and redder. Finally she stood beside the table of the four suburban ladies who had ordered the fatal chicken patties. The eyes of every customer in the tearoom were glued upon my distraught sister. With one accord all hands wondered how she would or could lower the chicken patties from their present height, about where you hold the ball before you throw it up to serve in tennis, down to table, or eating, level.

The chicken patty ladies sat rigid with horror while Eileen rocked the tray high above their heads. Finally Eileen said simply, but in a very loud voice, "HELP."

At this point chicken patty customer Number One gingerly clambered out of her seat, and with great presence of mind, grabbed her plate off the tray and got it down to the table without incident. Her three cronies also rose and safely slid their lunches out of Eileen's trembling hands. Eileen said afterwards she mentally fainted about this point so what happened afterwards, the hostess coming over and apologizing, and the customers being very sweet and poor-girling Eileen hardly mattered.

For some reason, Harvey's didn't fire Eileen after this, although they retired her to the extreme rear of the restaurant where sometimes she got as much as ten cents a day in tips. In spite of her slow "station," Eileen had plenty of other opportunities for mental fainting during her first week at the tearoom.

The second day we were working, the entire female section of the Farrel clan came trotting down to observe our technique and the quaint sight of Eileen making her own living. Seven aunts and four cousins in all made up the little party and the well-known Farrel sense of humor was at its best, or, to put it more accurately, at its loudest. Aunt Kate, who is the wit of the family, had brought her lunch, consisting as she said at the top of her voice of raw onion sandwiches and baloney, in a little tin work kit which she claimed Grandpa had carried to work the first four years he was married. Before the astounded and horrified eyes of the hostess and the rest of the trade, she settled right down near the fish fountain on the best red leather bench and loudly ordered a glass of beer to top off the onion sandwiches.

The hostess explained about prohibition and suggested in her iciest voice a glass of milk instead. Aunt Kate said since when was milk as good as beer, and after all she needed to keep up her strength, she was the champion floor scrubber in the whole Union Station. All the rest of the aunts kept saying, "Isn't Kate a card?" When the Farrels finally filed out we found they had left Confederate money, of which there was a great oversupply in the family, for tips. Eileen said she fainted mentally twice when Aunt Kate started to crack the shells of the hard-boiled eggs on the sole of her shoe.

The Harvey tearoom opened on Monday. On Wednesday my feet hurt so that nothing else in the world mattered. On Thursday the Chef threatened Eileen with a large meat knife because she scorned his suit. He was a Latin type and very romantic. On Friday the hostess, who was tall and thin and very snobbish because she came from New York, caught Eileen and me wolfing down the special twenty-five-cent chocolate fudge cake. We were supposed to have two-day-old pie for our own lunches but Eileen and I wangled the cake out of the pastry cook. On Saturday, Eileen finally dropped two orders of creamed mushrooms on toast. In a way it was sort of a relief. Everybody felt the worst was over.

Everybody was wrong. On the following Tuesday Eileen dropped two fruit salads with whipped creamed dressing and an order of fudge cake. She was afterwards caught in the kitchen demolishing the cake which she said was very little damaged.

On Friday Billy Hunnecker, the gorgeous lad aged eighteen came into our tearoom for lunch, trailing his mother and Eileen's friend, his sister Marge. At this point Eileen quit, leaving four customers talking to themselves about their creamed chicken on toast. I was fired five minutes later for sympathizing with her.

We tried to keep it from Father, but he soon sensed something was wrong, especially as the head waiter from the golf club called him up the very next day and asked him, in view of what had occurred the last time, if he wanted his daughter to sign restaurant checks.

Father said we were both destined for the poor house, especially Eileen, unless we married very great wealth which he very much doubted we would ever do. He said it would serve us both right if we did end up chewing the bitter bread of charity. Did Andrew Carnegie walk out on his first job because his beau turned up? Obviously not. On the whole, Father said in conclusion, he did not think we were the sturdy American pioneer type that fought its way from rags to riches.

Time, I regret to say, has proved him right.

The Gladsome Washing Machine Season

FATHER FEELS LIKE KING LEAR, WITH
GOOD REASON.

OTHER people may go around caroling about spring and violets and things, but Eileen and I regard the gladsome May season with considerable sourness. It makes us think of washing machines.

For my father used to hold himself in all during the blustery winter months, a little restless, but still fairly content with his *Saturday Evening Post* and a few rounds of bridge on Saturday nights. But come the first warm day, and Father was off on his quest of the perfect washing machine.

Father was a man of regular habits, and year after year, the storm always broke in exactly the same fashion. Father would come whistling down to breakfast, always a sign of trouble on the wing, and start off merrily with, "Well, well, well, I guess today's washing day, isn't it?"

He knew perfectly well it was, of course. The breakfast room was just over the section of the basement where already Belle, the laundress, was hard at work at the family washing machine. You could hear the groan and whine and swoosh of the machine with perfect distinctness as you gulped your morning shredded wheat.

"Yes, sir," Father would continue, not without a certain uneasy tone creeping into his voice, "I guess it certainly is washing day, all right, all right."

"Uhmmmmmmm," the whole family would murmur warily, in reply.

"Well, I guess today's just as good as any day to give a try to the new model." Father always blurted this out and then buried himself in Orphan Annie. A strict family rule forbade any interruption of the head of the house while he read the day's adventures of his favorite heroine.

When the argument finally did break out, Father was always very much grieved that none of his own kith and kin took the slightest interest in his career. Here he was, the manager of a home electric appliance factory ("Mother's Best Helper") and did his family care whether his new fall model washing machine was going to be a success or not? No. He worked himself to the bone, day and night, to provide food, and yes, luxuries for his little brood and look what he got in return! A lot of carping talk about whether Belle would quit or not if he brought the experimental model home. A man's own basement was no longer, he supposed, his castle. He liked Belle, but was Belle going to ruin his business career? He would be mighty sorry when we had Belle and no money to pay her with. You can't pay

Belle on what you get from selling pencils on street corners.

Besides, he absolutely guaranteed that this new model was past the experimental stage and it really would not squirt oil all over the best tablecloth like the spring before.

And for the last time, a laboratory was no place to give a final test to a washing machine. You needed practical home conditions to see if it would really stand up under the wear and tear housewives would give it next fall. Housewives are all dumb and continually pull the wrong lever and jam up the works and you need to see if a washing machine that works fine in a laboratory will stand the strain of a lot of feeble-minded women running it backwards all the time.

And, *for Heaven's sake*, nobody said anybody around here was dumb, can't a man explain a thing or two without starting a fight?

So about nine-fifteen that morning a large truck would draw up in our driveway and a crew of four or five husky men in oil-stained overalls would jump out and start to yell, "Easy, easy there, boys, they ain't got this thing screwed together very tight."

Neighbor ladies, tipped off by the sound of hearty

voices breaking the quiet of our suburban street, would rush out to their backyards, carrying trowels and garden rakes as decoys, the better to observe the McKenney family's annual struggle with the washing machine problem. Just as the leader of the crew bawled, "Set it down gentle, boys, set it down gentle, it's holdin' together by a hair!" Belle would appear at our side door.

Belle was a mild-mannered, dreamy Irish lady of undetermined age and manifold sorrows. Three suitors, including a policeman, had left our Belle waiting at the altar and life had inflicted a series of other outrages on the bloody and considerably bowed head of our unfortunate family retainer. Belle bore these blows of fate as best she could, and not without a lot of loud and off-key keening in our basement, but one thing our Belle could not abide—the annual washing machine experimental season.

For Belle, who was suspicious of machinery at its best, regarded Father's spring washing machine models as creatures of the devil, infernal contraptions invented by Satan himself to plague her poor old soul and body.

So she would meet the invasion of the trucking crew with flashing eyes and furious tongue. "And do my eyes deceive me," she used to screech, getting a good hand and even a few faint cheers from the rapidly growing backyard audience. Then she would point dramatically with her bony finger at the new model, now standing in the driveway, ready for its trip down the basement stairs.

"Stand aside!" the head of the trucking crew would bawl in reply, for he knew our Belle from last year. "Look out, or we'll trample yuh! We're takin' it down!"

Some years the new model blew up the moment Belle touched the motor button. There would be a five-minute silence after the truck and the delivery crew left, while Belle put a batch of clothes and the appropriate amounts of soap chips and hot water in the new machine, and then suddenly, as she turned the switch, a low roar, a grinding noise, and then a loud plop, plop, plop, followed by a hysterical shriek of bolts, gears, and motor, rising finally to a mighty climax with an explosion that rocked the neighborhood or anyhow the house next door. As quiet slowly settled down again, we could hear Belle saying her prayers in the coal bin, whither she had fled for refuge.

The disintegration of the new model was usually

not quite so rapid, however, although nearly always as spectacular. Sometimes Belle would get half the family washing done before a low peculiar whine caught her alert ear. She would leap to turn off the motor, not always before the whine blossomed into the mighty roar of the whole machine shaking apart before her very eyes. Other years, Belle would learn that something had gone a little wrong when she took the cover off the tub to remove the freshly washed clothes, only to find them floating in a sea of rich black oil.

But in the whole era of new spring experimental models, the washday never passed without Father being summoned home from his factory by his hysterical family. He would arrive on these occasions riding on the repair truck, with the entire experimental department in tow, including seven bright young men only recently from M.I.T. and four hard-bitten practical mechanics who had no use for the college geniuses. Father was a college engineer himself, but he had spent so many years running a factory that he rather leaned towards the anti-higher-education group in his experimental department.

The truck would pull up briskly beside the basement door and the enthralled neighbor ladies would watch twelve strong men and true march into the McKenney house, presumably to fix up one little old washing machine. Presently, by keeping a sharp ear cocked, they would hear the sound of bitter controversy leaking out from the basement windows. Men raised their voices in bold denial of bolder accusations.

"I told you this here differential ain't no good. You with your fancy ideas!" a hoarse voice would howl.

"Do I understand," a cultured but infuriated voice would scream in reply, "that you are blaming the differential on me? Really!"

After an hour's loud argument, one of the inventors would come brusquely up the stairs, stamp to the telephone without so much as a kind word for the assembled and anxious womenfolk, and, spreading a film of oil and grease over the living-room carpet, lean against the wallpaper as he juggled the receiver professionally against a dirty ear. The wallpaper always had to be cleaned after the washing machine season.

"Hello," the young man would growl, "listen, that bunch of saps in my department thinks we got a little differential trouble in the new model. So send us over some parts, will yuh?"

Then he would name off various high-sounding contraptions while Belle would be at his elbow, demanding, "How soon are they going to get it fixed? I got to get my washing done."

Getting the washing done was always the least of Father's troubles. After several hours' work, Father would bawl up the basement stairs, ordering sandwiches and beer and other nutritious items for himself and his crew which had now expanded considerably. For the man who brought the parts also arrived in a truck with two other gentlemen from some obscure department in the factory, who stuck around to see what was up. Then one of the executives of the company, getting word of the trouble, would arrive in a big Packard. By late afternoon the McKenney driveway would be crowded with trucks, Packards, and other vehicles, while the basement would be swarming with inventors, toolmakers, mechanics, worried general managers, excited sales managers, and Father. The neighbors of course would be beside themselves with curiosity. God knows what was happening, they used to twitter, in the McKenney basement!

138

At last, as dusk fell, all hands would admit temporary defeat and the trucking crew would reappear to haul the poor new model, now considerably denuded, back to the factory. With a roar of motors and the grinding of many sets of gears, the little band of inventors, company executives, and mechanics would depart, leaving Belle mourning over a pile of dirty clothes in the basement.

Some years it took five different tries to get the experimental model to run through a day's washing. Before Father's inventors finally solved their differential trouble, Belle would be driven to the verge of giving notice, the neighbors would decide we were hatching a Guy Fawkes plot, and the Cleveland Heights Flat and Fancy Laundry Company, Inc., would get plenty of rush trade from the McKenney family. But eventually peace and calm would settle down over the basement regions of the household. Belle would resign herself to doing the washing all year on the now renovated experimental model, which still lacked the coat of paint and other trimmings the commercial machine would sport next fall, and Father's fancy would turn from washing machines to vacuum cleaners.

We always had four big vacuum cleaners and two

small ones, big ones for the attic, second floor, first floor, and basement, hand cleaners for the bedrooms and living room. We had so many vacuum cleaners we had to spend a fortune in getting new electric outlets put in the house. Father used to play around with his vacuum cleaners even in the winter season and we often used to watch him in the attic, solemnly running the machine up and down between trunks and boxes of old family pictures, listening to the roar of the motor with a thoughtful and attentive ear.

But when spring came and the washing machine flurry was over, Father would double our quota of electric sweepers. The house would be overrun with vacuum cleaners in all stages of repair and disrepair, and one Maytime a distant second cousin, paying a formal call, got a bad sprain falling over a whole nest of new model sweepers. Many is the time I have quietly sneaked down the stairs at night and found Father sprinkling the best carpet with tacks, soap chips, cotton batting, bits of artificial hair cut up fine, and grapefruit seeds. Grapefruit seeds are slippery and no mean test for any vacuum cleaner. Father would attack these assorted challenges with two vacuum cleaners, one in each hand, often stopping long before the last soap chip had disappeared, to tinker with a motor or take apart the insides of a revolving brush.

We didn't mind the vacuum cleaner season so much, though, even if Annie, the cleaning girl, had to chase stray grapefruit seeds and odd sections of motors and revolving brushes around the living room for weeks after Father had finally decided on the new fall model. For Father's family had the opportunity of sharing some of the delightful notions of the M.I.T. geniuses that never survived to hit the public eye. One spring, for instance, all the vacuum cleaners in the house were painted red, white, and blue in startling zebra stripes. Father kept running the cleaners up and down and asking us above the roar of the motors if we thought they looked patriotic.

Another year, two of our downstairs vacuum cleaners had a type of asthma which Eileen and I considered diverting but which drove the adults in the household close to madness. When you pushed the cleaners forward the motors gave out a loud rattle, and when you pulled them back, they sounded like dying men fighting for their last breath. That same season the three attic cleaners all snored, in the slow intake and bubbling outlet manner.

The best vacuum cleaner spring of all, however, was the delightful year when Father's newest inventor equipped three experimental models in the McKenney household with revolving locomotive headlights and musical auto horns. It was a positive pleasure to run one of those sweepers. With a little practice, you could spring a surprise attack on some unwary adult, blinding him with the spotlight and scaring him out of two years' growth with the blast of the horn, at one and the same moment. Eileen practiced up and one night made Father the victim of her most skillful vacuum cleaner foray. After that Father discarded the notions of musical horns and reduced the headlight to mere flashlight size, stationary at that. He also considered firing the new inventor.

But even musical horns on vacuum cleaners paled beside the most spectacular Maytime in McKenney history, the happy season when Father played around with the notion of manufacturing an electrical reducing machine. The family suspected that Father had something up his sleeve that spring. The washing machine season bloomed and died away in three short works, a record, and Father took only an apathetic interest in his new crop of vacuum cleaners.

Finally, on a warm May night, Father brought the experimental model of the new reducer home from the factory. With a modest, nay, sheepish, smile, but a look of unguarded triumph in his eye, he led his little family to the bathroom where, with a few deft turns of a screwdriver and a bit of fussing around with some wires, he installed the device which he announced would revolutionize American ladies' figures.

The embryo American ladies in Father's family took one look at the sinister machine now occupying large spaces of the bathroom and announced in one voice it would probably kill a horse. Father said that showed you. King Lear had nothing on him. His own daughters refused to even try his reducing machine.

Father's family was firm. All those belts and wooden rollers and iron hands! If this thing worked like the new washing machine, God knows what would happen to the unwary victim caught in its toils.

Father scoffed. His new reducer couldn't hurt a baby. In fact, it would be good for a baby, harden him up. It had three-way action, too. It reproduced exactly the effects of riding a horse, playing leapfrog, and stretching, all at one and the same moment. It was scientific. And all you had to do was to climb inside the various pulleys and belts, switch on the motor, and stand still. The machine did the rest.

"You try it, Father," we all said sweetly.

So, stung by the jesting, and even cynical, remarks of his daughters, Father stepped into the maze of belts and rollers and, stubborn to the last, turned the switch. His final words, before the roar of the motor drowned him out were, "Three-way action, gentle as a kitten, firm and efficient as an expensive masseuse."

Father always claimed that his family deliberately let him be shaken out of ten years of his life, just to win an argument. It really wasn't true, though. We couldn't hear Father screaming for help because the airplane motor attached to the belts and rollers and things blanketed out every other noise in the world. Father's lean body, it was true, was shaking like a small leaf in a first-class hurricane, but how was his devoted family to guess that he was literally imprisoned in a whirlwind of revolving belts, rollers, and iron hands? He had turned the motor switch on, we thought he would turn it off when he had had enough.

So we just stood by, marveling at Father's resistance, while, as he bitterly said afterwards, he was being ground to dust under our very noses. Eileen finally noticed that Father's eyes had begun to glaze and that he seemed to be trying to reach out a palsied hand towards the motor switch.

We put Father to bed with a glass of warm milk and four aspirins. He twitched dreadfully at first and apparently he had lost the power of speech forever. All he could do was roll his eyes. Gradually however his twitches faded into gentle trembles and about 10 P.M. his low groans developed into a stutter.

"G-get a d-d-doctor!" he was able to cry.

Father said afterwards, when he was restored to apparent good health, hardly the worse for his spectacular wear, that the trouble with some inventors he could mention was that they let enthusiasm run riot over reason.

It was, the family thought, something of an understatement.

The Prince

SENTIMENTAL STORY ABOUT AN AGRICUL-
TURIST.

ONE of my earliest beaux was a Georgian prince who came from the same general neighborhood as the Mdivanis. He was, however, a simple fellow with annoying habits. His first name was Gregory. He was studying dairy science at Ohio State University when I met him, and if his stock of stolen diamonds is holding out, he probably still is. He was simply fascinated by dairy science and talked about it constantly. In fact, we parted over that issue.

One night I said firmly, "Say, listen, if you can't talk about anything but cows, you may as well go home."

He went, looking hurt. He was a big eater, too, and my grandmother used to complain bitterly. He dropped in for dinner so often we took to ordering three chops instead of two as a regular practice. He used to demolish a whole batch of butter cookies in one evening, carrying on a steady flow of small talk about breeding cows, in between bites.

He was handsome enough, if you like that dark, beady type. Personally, one Georgian prince was enough for me. Every time I now see a pair of what Grandmother used, scornfully, to call "snake" eyes, I shudder. I met Gregory at an Engineers' Frolic. He never explained what he, an earnest dairy-science student, was doing at an engineers' dance, but at the time I didn't ask. I foolishly thought he was quite a catch—handsome, and with a title, too, even if slightly shopworn. After all, Georgian princes were distinctly *comme il faut* in 1930, and even Eileen, the belle of the Midwest, hadn't been able to gather in, during her heart-smashing career, so much as a Belgian count.

Gregory, however, was disappointing from the first. He didn't talk much about Georgia, for instance; he said the subject bored him. He settled down on the sofa, that first evening he called, and began firmly, "Since I have been a leetle boy, people have been asking me about how I escape, how I get to this country, what happen to Papa, and all the rest of it. Well, I tell you wance and then we shut oop about the subject, yes?"

I said, "Yes," slightly dazed, and he recited rapidly, in a bored tone, the more salient points in his explosive career. He had been a lad of tender years, ten or eleven, when the revolution broke out. For many years his canny father had been expecting the worst. All the family wealth was in loose diamonds, except for a few scattered sheep. But alas for Papa and Gregory when they went to look for the diamonds! It turned out the Georgian equivalent of the butler had stolen them all. This left the fledgling prince and his father and other relatives, very numerous, in something of a hole. But Father was a quick thinker. He went over to the next castle and stole the neighbors' supply of diamonds.

"All it ees fair," Gregory remarked at this point in his recital, "in luff and war." This gave me food for reflection. If Gregory conducted his love affairs in the same spirit in which his family conducted wars, obviously he was a man who would bear close watching.

As it turned out, however, the neighbors didn't need their diamonds, anyway. They were killed, the whole lot of them.

"They were very what you call mean to the poor people," Gregory said simply, "so they all get killed."

Gregory paused at this point in his recital, perhaps for effect, perhaps for a moment's painful reflection. Then he said, "All our family got killed too, except me. I hide in a big drawer."

I said, "My!"

He replied, "Yes, our family was also mean to what you call the poor people. They kick tham around, no?"

151

I said I supposed he was pretty down on the Communists.

"I was," he agreed, nodding, "but I am not any more, cause they have got the only gud onderstanding of dairy science of any government in the whole wurld, yes. They have got posi-tive *mir*-acles of dairy farms. Such people that onderstand dairy science, they cannot be wrong, no? But just the same," Gregory added, chuckling, "if I should ever meet any of those paysants who murdered my papa, I would keel tham right off. But I stay out of their way, no?" He laughed uproariously, slapping his knee.

"So then what happened to you?" I said, bringing him back to his story.

"Oh," he said, the interest dying out of his heavy voice, "oh, then I escape, with the diamonds, and, believe me, it was pretty hard work for a leetle fellow like I was. But soon I met some fellow from my home town. He was also ronning away, and I went with him, only he stole all my diamonds—he was a no-good, believe me."

"How did you live?" I cried in anxiety.

"I stole tham back, and all of his, too," Gregory said simply.

Finders keepers was a game with prestige in Georgia, I gathered. Poor little Gregory had a bad time escaping from his native land. He hid in a camel's pack, stowed away on a Soviet vessel, rode across the Arabian desert, was captured by the Turkish equivalent of the juvenile court, and spent two years in a Moslem orphanage. Finally he ended up, triumphant, in Berlin, still with most of his diamonds.

"Although I was only feevteen then," Gregory said sadly, "already I was a man of the wurld, so much it had happened to me."

I understood, I said. "So then I traveled," Gregory continued. "I go to *Ee*taly, to Paris, to London, to Holland. I see much, but I don' like. I get older, but nawthing suit me, nawthing please me."

It was a pathetic picture, a poor little homesick Georgian princeling, living on the neighbors' diamonds, traveling from one world capital to another, always bored, always sad. It brought a tear to my sympathetic eye.

"Weemin!" Gregory intoned in his guttural bass, "Wine! Sung! All it ees vanity."

I sighed and he sighed.

"I was twenty-two," Gregory said, finally, coming to what he thought was the climax of his story, "when I discover dairy science. Since then I have been happy, almost."

I was so shocked by this dairy-science revelation that it took me some time to ask him, "Almost?"

"Two things," Gregory said promptly, "keep me from being happy. One, I cannot go to the Soviet Union to see the dairy farms, the best in the whole wurld; and two, I have not got a wife."

At this point he looked firmly at me with what I considered an evil gleam in those black eyes of his. There was something fearfully direct about Gregory; it gave you quite a turn. "That's tough about Russia," I said hastily. "What's the matter? Won't they let you in?"

"I have not ask," he said, "but of course they could not. I might see some of those paysants who cut up my papa, and then I would have to keel tham."

"Russia is a big country," I said helpfully. "Besides, how would they know you were going to kill anybody?"

"I would have to tell tham," Gregory said sorrowfully.

He paused, thinking, no doubt, of the horrid

scene: a famous dairy scientist, full of Communist honors, caught red-handed in the murder of a fellow-worker, and a political murder, at that.

"Yess," he said heavily, "if I keel tham, it would set back dairy science in the Soviet Union tan years, easy."

His remark fell into a nervous silence.

"Well," Gregory added, after several minutes had ticked by uncomfortably, "well, fife."

I looked up at him, startled. It was a mistake. "Now how about the sweedhard, the wife?" he cried, with heavy humor.

I had some difficulty getting rid of Gregory that first night he called, and if I had had any sense I would never again have let him in the quiet apartment my grandmother and I occupied together. But there was a touch, to put it mildly, of the exotic about Gregory, and I was nineteen. Exotics appealed to me then. They did not, however, appeal to my grandmother, especially Gregory.

"You remide me," Gregory said to her one night, "of an old Armenian lady I knew wance, log ago."

"Indeed?" said my grandmother, who looks extremely young for her age, and who has her hair and nails done every week.

"Yes," Gregory said, a merry twinkle in his eye. "The Turks, they smawthered her to death. Like this." He rose, seized a soft pillow, and energetically ground it into the carpet with his knee.

My grandmother paled, but her perfect manners did not fail her. "How interesting," she murmured. It was a mistake, a bad one.

"You thank so?" Gregory chuckled, pleased. "That's nawthing. You should see what they do to the young ones." He took out a knife, whipped it open, and was apparently prepared to slice up the sofa pillow when my grandmother, gulping hard, diverted his interest.

From the first night on, Gregory kept pressing me on the question of the wife, and I kept making coy excuses until one night, in desperation, I told him a fearful lie. "Alas," I said earnestly, "I am already engaged."

"Yes?" Gregory asked, his beady black eyes fixed firmly on my face. So, having told one whopper, I went on, as is my unhappy custom, and told several more. Gregory sat in what I thought was saddened silence while I recited a pathetic tale of woe. My father was making me marry this youth, in whom I had only the slightest interest, so that Eileen could have a college education.

When I finished this sorry story, Gregory rose energetically. "It ees easy," he said, shrugging his shoulders. "I keel him, yes?"

"I should say not," I said hastily, stunned by this unusual turn of affairs. "My!"

Gregory ignored my protests. He was an overbearing type, anyway. "You tell me his name, his address," he said gruffly, "and after this term final examination, and after Elizabeth she is calved, I keel him."

I was stung. To think he would put Elizabeth, his experimental Jersey, ahead of killing his rival! Chivalry, I felt, was dead, even among Georgian princes. Elizabeth's time was some weeks off, however, and I felt fairly easy in my mind.

Unfortunately, my tranquillity was soon shattered, because, shortly after, Robbin showed up. Robbin played a brief but dramatic role in my relations with Gregory, and I fear that I will have to explain him, disagreeable as that task is. Even now, looking back on Robbin, I can't think why I ever liked him, even for a moment. Youth does not explain everything.

Robbin was pale, blond, and pimply. He was a graduate of Georgia Tech, and he never let you forget it for a moment. He was constantly singing a vile song that begins, "I'm a ramblin' wreck from Georgia Tech." Also, Robbin had written across the back of his very yellow raincoat—a garment he wore constantly, rain or no rain—the legend "Georgia Tech 27, Alabama 0." I'm not sure of the exact figures, but that was the general idea. Everywhere I went with Robbin, this sign printed on his back caused the most unpleasant kind of remarks from taxicab drivers, soda jerkers, and the like.

Robbin lived in Cleveland, and I had met him a few days before I left for Columbus to go back to college. Thus our romance was brief. I forgot all about him until the awful Saturday night when he appeared at our Columbus apartment, smiling toothily. It seems he wanted to surprise me. He certainly did. The moment I saw him, I thought of Gregory, my tiger prince, and the fearful lie I had told him. Gregory had a habit of just dropping in. Suppose he found Robbin sitting on the davenport with me?

Robbin had dinner with us that terrible night, and I couldn't eat, I was so panic-stricken. Grandmother, who was a model of tact, then announced she was going to the movies with the lady who lived downstairs, and she supposed we would be going out, later in the evening. Robbin all but clapped hands. Apparently this suited his plans perfectly.

"No," I said, my hand shaking on my coffee cup. "No, you stay home, Grandma. Don't you go anywhere. Please don't!" I felt that if anybody could stay Gregory's murderous hand, it would be Grandma.

Grandma blinked in surprise, but she stayed home. It turned out afterward that she had drawn the wrong conclusions. She thought I was afraid of Robbin, who was actually the most harmless of men, and she stayed firmly in the living room all evening, keeping a stern eye on the man she thought I thought was a beast.

Robbin was pretty dashed. He kept suggesting all through the early part of the evening that we should go dancing or walking or go to the movies. Grandmother, however, said firmly that I wasn't to put a foot outside the house *that* night.

The whole situation was so hopelessly confused I didn't think that even if I took Grandma out in the kitchen and explained everything to her, I could make it clear. So I just sat miserably on the sofa with Robbin and waited for the inevitable. About ten o'clock, Gregory came thumping up the stairs.

I opened the door. I smiled weakly. "Hello," I said faintly.

He stalked in, looking neither to the right nor left. "Such a day!" he said, breathing hard. "I can only stay a minute. I came to tell you that Elizabeth, she ees sick." With that he sank down dramatically on the sofa, right beside Robbin, who jumped slightly.

"This is Mr. Wilkins," I said, breathlessly. "Robbin, this is Prince Gregory."

"Prince, eh?" Robbin said brightly.

Gregory ignored the introduction. "She ees very sick. I think it ees the weather. She ees so delicad."

"That's too bad," my grandmother murmured politely.

"You feel bad, eh?" Gregory said, brightening up. "I also feel bad. It hurts me in the heart to see Elizabeth so sick like she ees." He turned to me, and said accusingly, "She ees in pain, but you don' care, eh?"

I said I did too care; I felt very sad about Elizabeth. Gregory turned to Robbin. "You care for cows?" he asked heavily.

"Sure," Robbin, who was a weakling and afraid to cross anybody, replied.

There was a pause. Nobody felt like starting a new and happier theme of conversation. Suddenly Gregory turned on Robbin. He looked him right in the eye. "Who are *you?*" he roared. My heart nearly stopped. "Ha!" he said, leaping to his feet. "You are *heem!*"

"I am *not,*" Robbin said hastily, to be on the safe side, and added, "What's the big idea, anyway?"

"No, no," I shouted desperately, "he isn't! Really he isn't!" My grandmother and Robbin goggled.

"Yes," Gregory said with sinister emphasis, "yes, I can see who you are now." Robbin turned much paler than his usual pasty white. He shook his head in terrified denial, too frightened to speak. He certainly didn't make a very good showing in the whole affair.

My grandmother, however, rose to the occasion. "Gregory," she said calmly, although she thought she was addressing a madman, "don't you think you ought to stay with Elizabeth if she is so ill?"

"I am thinging of Elizabeth," Gregory said slowly.

161

"I am trying to figure out if I got time to feex heem before I go back to Elizabeth."

I kept moaning, "He isn't the one, he isn't the one," but Gregory, as usual, paid no attention to me. He just stood there, a mighty figure of a man, think-- ing, while Robbin turned piteous eyes to me for an explanation of this awful situation.

"No," Gregory said finally, "I have not the time. I must go." He seized his hat, bowed, and went to the door. "I find you," he said to Robbin, who huddled, shaking with fear, in the sofa pillows, "lader on." We all heard him thumping down the stairs.

Robbin left Columbus on the milk train, absolutely unimpressed by my sincere explanations. He said, frankly, that he thought I was perfectly terrible for letting him in for an experience like that.

"You better look out," he said darkly, as he left. "I'm going to write a letter as soon as I get home and give it to my lawyer, in case anything happens to me. You'll be an accomplice, under the law."

That was just like Robbin, a worm of the first water, selfish to the last. Elizabeth recovered, un- fortunately, and that was really why my Georgian prince and I parted. I felt that he thought more of Elizabeth than he did of me.

"Yes," Gregory said heavily, just before the end, "I guess I am wadded to my science."

It was a curious choice of bride, for a Georgian prince.

The Sock Hunt

ALL ABOUT MR. RANDOLPH CHURCHILL,
BREATH OF EMPIRE.

I SUPPOSE, what with the passing years and the girls he's met since, that young Mr. Randolph Churchill, the scion of the London Churchills, does not remember me. Still, looking back on it all, I should think he would. I certainly do. Precisely as I can never, for so long as I walk this earth, forget the time I fell down at my high-school senior prom, right smack in front of the orchestra with my best beau and only sprawled beside me, so can I never put aside the memory of young Mr. Churchill. My flesh still crawls. Not that Mr. Churchill is anything to make a girl's flesh crawl. Not at all. In a certain way, like the men in the breakfast-food ads, he is quite handsome.

Mr. Churchill and I met in a purely professional capacity. It was the late fall of 1930. He was touring America, speaking before literary clubs, Rotary Clubs, university clubs, and the like on a variety of light topics, including "Fate of an Empire" and "Why I Am a Conservative." He was then nineteen, and I was the daisy-eyed star reporter on the *Ohio State Lantern*, a newspaper published daily, except Saturday and Sunday, by the students of journalism at Ohio State University.

Young Mr. Churchill arrived in Columbus, Ohio, on the flood tide of a lot of awe-struck advance notices. He was to address a local men's dinner club which for pure hauteur would make the Union Club look sick any day. All the speeches before this tony outfit were dead secret; no reporters allowed. Furthermore, celebrities who appeared before these hallowed few were never interviewed by the Columbus press. The editors of the papers were all members of the club, and that was that.

Well, my mouth watered to interview Mr. Churchill. I had never seen a real Englishman in the flesh, for one thing. For another thing, my deadly rival on the *Lantern* staff, a chap of considerable energy and no ethics, had publicly stated that he considered the feat of obtaining an interview with Mr. Churchill too great even for his remarkable talents. After this, nothing could hold me. I marched forward with determination to my doom.

I arrived at the hotel lobby at 4:35 P.M. and briskly set about finding out Mr. Churchill's room number. Then, with success almost in the hollow of my hand, I collapsed on a lobby lounge with an attack of acute panic. This lasted until 5:22 P.M., when a man insulted me. At least he came directly over to my lounge and said, in a chummy tone, "Waiting for somebody?"

This drove me to Mr. Churchill. I fled from my insulter and arrived at the forbidding door of Mr. Churchill's hotel room, still unnerved. I knocked valiantly. I had mapped out my strategy well in advance. When Mr. Churchill asked, "Who's there?" I intended to reply, "Maid, with towels." Then, when he opened the door, I planned to stick my foot in the crack and ask him a lot of questions very fast. I think a scene such as this had been in a newspaper film about that time.

Anyway, Mr. Churchill ruined my pretty plans by replying, to the knock, "Come in." I hesitated, getting a burning sensation in my throat. I was nineteen and lived with my grandmother, who would have been absolutely horrified at the thought of any young woman traipsing into a man's hotel room alone.

"Come IN!" roared Mr. Churchill from behind the door. He sounded rather angry. I kept telling myself that after I got out of school and got a real job on a newspaper, I would look back on this moment and laugh. As it turned out, however, in spite of a lot of jobs on newspapers, genuine daily ones, the mere thought of that frightful moment, with Mr. Churchill bellowing "Come IN" on one side of the door and me trembling on the other, has

169

never brought even the sickliest of smiles to my face. It still makes my hair prickle.

Finally I opened the door very timidly indeed, and beheld Mr. Churchill, surely the blondest young man in the world, seated at a desk, writing. He wore a smoking jacket over his dinner trousers, black vest, and starched shirt front. His bare feet were stuck in floppy leather slippers. Mr. Churchill looked so very public-school English he was faintly incredible. Maybe he's grown out of that now, but in 1930 he was certainly breath of Empire. You could—or at least I could—just see him wolfing down supper off in the tropics, dressed to the teeth in tails and white tie. Mr. Churchill's eyes were a china blue and his smoking jacket was the same, overlaid, however, with old rose and gold.

I stood by the door for several seconds while Mr. Churchill continued to scratch away at his desk. Now, a cynical old interviewer of ripened years, I fear that Mr. Churchill was attempting to impress me. But on that trying evening I felt that I had intruded on the literary labors of a young genius. Finally Mr. Churchill lifted his blue eyes to mine.

"Ah," he said, leaping gallantly to his feet, "a lady! I beg your pardon. Pray do forgive me."

170

My mouth sagged. Mr. Churchill drew up a chair beside his desk and, with a cozy gesture, beckoned me over. I went.

"Pray excuse me," said Mr. Churchill. "I must finish this wireless message." On his desk lay eleven or twelve Western Union blanks covered with writing.

"What?" I said. The reason I said this was that I could not understand very much of what he said. His accent, which I had so longed to hear, a real, bona-fide Oxford accent, was so broad that unfortunately he might as well have spoken French. I can get every other word a Frenchman says, too, which is fairly good, considering I studied French in the Ohio public schools for only eight years.

Young Mr. Churchill now turned to me and said in a fierce tone, "What would you say if you wanted to tell your manager you did not want ladies to give you flowers at lectures?" At least that is what I thought he said. It was so difficult for me to decipher Mr. Churchill's accent, and the question seemed so entirely improbable, that, after agonized reflection, I simply shook my head.

Mr. Churchill didn't note my silence. He apparently hit on just the right words, for he signed his

171

name with a flourish I am sure no American operator ever spelled out, and turned briskly to me, saying, "Now, what may I do for you?"

I explained haltingly that I was a newspaper reporter. Mr. Churchill didn't ask, so I didn't find it necessary to tell him that the paper I was interviewing him for was only, alas, the university daily. I simply trotted out all my carefully prepared questions. I asked him about Ramsay MacDonald and Hoover and Briand and a few other such people. Mr. Churchill roundly denounced them all, for different reasons. MacDonald was too far left, and even Mr. Hoover was pretty much of a Socialist. I asked him about the future of English youth, and Mr. Churchill said that if only a few more young people of his class would awaken to their responsibility, the future of England was safe. I was slightly shaken at Mr. Churchill's firm Tory opinions. He seemed quite young to be so fierce.

However, I drew a breath and started off on the English public-school system. Just at this point Mr. Churchill created a diversion.

In an ordinary speaking voice, as distinguished from the voice in which he denounced Mr. Hoover or Mr. MacDonald, he said, "Would you care for a drink?"

This unnerved me again. I could explain the interview to Grandma and my conscience, but drinking with a total stranger in his hotel room certainly seemed excessive. In those days, most college students —at least at my school—still thought drinking, no matter where, was pretty darned daring. Mr. Churchill, however, had already unearthed from his suitcase a bottle of what he assured me was fine Scotch, straight from England.

I was no judge. Up to that very moment I had never tasted anything in alcoholic beverages except a variety of bootleg liquor distilled in some abandoned mines near New Straitsville, Ohio. New Straitsville corn burned your throat and made you sick. Also, it hurt so to choke down New Straitsville corn that you were acutely conscious of every drink. It was the suave, sneaking quality of Mr. Churchill's fine liquor which undid me. You hardly knew you were drinking it, until afterward.

Mr. Churchill and I soon forgot serious topics. I asked him whether he really enjoyed lecturing about "Fate of an Empire." He said he did not, and also that he hated America and couldn't wait to get home. After a while Mr. Churchill thought we ought to eat something.

"I say," he said, "how about a spot of food, what?" He really talked just like that.

"O.K.," I said. "Let me order, though. They can't understand you over the phone. You talk so funny."

Mr. Churchill glowered. He said I was the one who had a peculiar accent.

"You talk through your nose," he said, with truth, "and you pronounce all your 'r's. They aren't supposed to be pronounced."

"That's what you think," I said, feeling hilarious, "Old Mushmouth."

For some reason, Mr. Churchill thought that was very funny. " 'Mushmouth!' " he shouted joyously, amid peals of real upper-class English laughter, very high-pitched, like a whinny. " 'Mushmouth!' Deah me, I must remembaw that."

We ate lamb chops, a lot of them. "Tell them to send up a bally lot of them!" Mr. Churchill roared while I telephoned. "I want six lamb chops all for myself. After all, I must lecture on the 'Fate of an Empire.' "

While we were gnawing on lamb-chop bones we

traded opinions on moving pictures. Mr. Churchill
was a fan, and so was I. It turned out we both adored
Vilma Banky. Suddenly Mr. Churchill said, "What
about my lecture?"

"Well," I said, "what about it?"

"I won't do it," Mr. Churchill said. "Let the
Empire go rot for tonight. Let's go to the cinema.
You and I."

For a moment I was sorely tempted. Then I pic-
tured the fearful scandal. The lecturer disappears.
The town's leading citizens are left waiting. Among
the leading citizens was the publisher of the Columbus *Dispatch*. I was the campus correspondent for
the Columbus *Dispatch*, and I lived—in a very
meager way, to be sure, but still I lived—on the
weekly wages the *Dispatch* paid me. In my fancy I
saw the publisher of the *Dispatch* discovering that
his most minor employee had practically kidnapped
young Mr. Churchill.

"No," I said firmly. "You have to make that
speech."

Mr. Churchill sighed. "Well, then," he said, "I
have to put on my dinner jacket." He found that all
right; also his white scarf and his black overcoat and
his two patent-leather pumps. But alas, as the hour

approached nine, he could find only one black sock. The club was to send a committee at nine, to escort Mr. Churchill to the lecture hall.

"What shall I do?" Mr. Churchill inquired frantically. "I can't lecture with only one sock." I rose from the dinner table, still gnawing a bone, and cast a quick look over the room.

"Be calm," I said. "They'll never notice."

"Oh, yes, they will," Mr. Churchill said. "Besides, I won't go unless we find that sock. And I only have one black pair with me. The rest of them are in Pittsburgh."

"Wear another color," I said lightly. "What happened to the socks you had on this afternoon?"

"Tan socks," Mr. Churchill shouted, "with a dinner coat?"

I observed Mr. Churchill's frenzy with a motherly eye. "There, there," I said. "Relax. I'll find it."

Mr. Churchill sat down, putting a childish faith in me. I failed. I trotted around in circles, afraid to look in his luggage—for after all, that would hardly be proper—and unable to spot a stray black sock in the immediate surroundings.

Suddenly Mr. Churchill shouted, "I bet it's under the bed. I unpacked my things on the bed, and maybe it fell off on the floor." He threw himself down beside his bed and stuck his head under the springs.

"I can't see it," he said dismally, sounding muffled. "You have a look from the other side."

I obligingly sprawled out under the wall side of the bed, and peered around, coughing in the dust. At this moment precisely, there was a knock on the door.

"Come in!" bellowed Mr. Churchill, before he thought. I gave a faint scream, and too late Mr. Churchill considered the informality of his position. He tried to get up, too suddenly, and bumped his head severely on the bed slats. He relapsed, groaning, just as the committee of super-leading citizens walked in.

Fortunately, I do not now remember the names of those three well-starched, beautifully tailored citizens who marched in on that sock-hunting expedition. It would be frightful to be haunted all my life by their names as well as their faces.

"Mr. Churchill?" said the first leading citizen, in a tone of pained surprise.

Young Mr. Churchill showed the heritage of generations of gentlemen. Still reclining on the floor, he turned his head, nodded an acknowledgment, and said in a loud, belligerent voice, "I'm looking for my lost black sock." The second leading citizen went directly to the bureau and picked up the lost black sock.

"Your sock, sir," he said. Mr. Churchill rose, bowed slightly, and said, "I thank you very much." Then he shouted to me, "Get up! We've found it."

I hesitated. I wanted to stay under that bed and just die there peacefully, without ever having to rise and face those three leading citizens. I did get up, though, feeling the way you do in dreams when you have no clothes on at a gala performance of "Aïda" in the Metropolitan. I suppose, from the expression on the faces of the three leading citizens, that they had not realized until the moment my face slowly emerged from behind the bed that there was a young lady in the room. Each leading citizen did a combination gasp and snort.

"She's coming to hear my lecture," Mr. Churchill announced as he put on his sock. The purple staining my cheeks now rose to my hairline.

"I couldn't," I said weakly. "I couldn't indeed. It's private. They don't allow women in."

"Nevertheless," said Mr. Churchill briskly, "I don't speak unless you come."

The three leading citizens looked so grim ⋏

thought I should really faint, although I never had in my whole life. Mr. Churchill and I and the committee now left the room and boarded the elevator. All the way down, Mr. Churchill maintained his position. I was to come or he wouldn't speak. The three leading citizens took turns saying, "But that is impossible, Mr. Churchill. The rules of the club do not permit ladies."

As we got off the elevator, one of the leading citizens, a tall, white-haired man with a large stomach, managed to fall in step with me while the two other leading citizens took Mr. Churchill by the arms.

"Now," said my sudden escort, "you go away fast, and stop bothering Mr. Churchill."

"Me?" I said in honest astonishment. "I never bothered him."

The leading citizen did not stop to argue. "Go away," he hissed, giving me a slight push into the lobby. I went. I was never so glad to leave any place in my life. I wrote my interview that night, and it was a big success. My rival, Ernest, was a picture of jealous confusion when he read it next day. But even the sweet rewards of college fame and my colleagues' envy did not erase the memory of that hideous moment when I was caught, red-handed, looking for Mr. Churchill's sock. It is comparatively easy to recover from honest sorrows, but I wake up in the dead of night at least twice a year and my heart fills with agony, remembering that unspeakable moment when, like a rising moon, my face slowly appeared from behind Mr. Churchill's bed, to confound the three leading citizens of Columbus, Ohio.

Life can hold no further terrors for me.

Spy Scare

A TERRIBLE EXPERIENCE I HAD IN POLAND.

I HAVE a great deal of sympathy for international spies, in and out of the movies. I know how inconvenient, how frequently awkward and distressing, their line of work can be, because I was thrown out of Poland once myself as a spy's accomplice.

The suspected spy was my best friend, a beautiful girl named Gerda, who had very little interest in international politics, either amateur or professional. In fact, I think I can state definitely that she was not, as the Polish Secret Service believed, in the pay of Foreign Powers. Certainly, if she was, they were wasting their money.

Gerda had been my roommate at Ohio State University for two years before we went to Europe, and she was so busy being Queen of the Engineers' Frolic she didn't have a moment, I assure you, to waste on spying. Besides, everybody knows that Columbus, Ohio, is a poor place for spying. A spy should find out things about Washington or West Point and places like that, and not go off on tangents like Columbus.

Well, anyway, to get back to the Polish Secret Service and their crude and mistaken notions about us, they apparently operated on the theory that they couldn't be too careful about who got into their nasty little country. They believed, it appeared, that nobody in his right mind came to Poland except to blow the place up, and after what happened to us, I can understand that idea. But we started for Poland with the most innocent of intentions. We were going to visit an old aunt of Gerda's who still grimly occupied the ancestral manor house and stubbornly administered what was left of the ancestral acres, which was not much.

Gerda's family was exceedingly aristocratic and exceedingly Austrian, and before the Polish Republic, they had owned several hundred Polish peasants outright, and a lot of land besides. The rest of the clan hastily moved out of Poland when the Poles started running the country, but Gerda's aunt held on, determined to be a nuisance to the Polish government, which she disliked very much indeed. I only mention this because the Poles do not like Austrians and Gerda's aunt may have had something to do with our little trouble, although I don't think so.

Our spy scare started promptly at 5:27 A.M., when our train pulled up at the Polish border for customs inspection. I was pretty groggy from an all-night ride on the wooden third-class compartment bench, and Gerda fell asleep the moment the train stopped jerk-

ing her neck. I watched, bleary-eyed, while the customs officer was very rude to the two Frenchmen and
assorted other aliens in our compartment. I handed
him my American passport with a weary gesture, and
as Gerda was still sleeping, I dug out her British
passport and gave him that, too. The reason Gerda
had a British passport was because she was born in
London, and her father had never been able to be
naturalized in America because he was born in Tur-
key at the home of the Austrian consul there and
nobody in our immigration department could figure
out whether that made him an Austrian or a Turk.

The customs man took a look at Gerda's passport
and then he looked at Gerda, who was really very
pretty, even when asleep. Then he stared fiercely at
me and I stared right back. I hated him, in advance
of our little trouble. Then he said to me, slowly and
distinctly, in German, which in those days I sometimes understood, "She is a spy. You are her dupe,
her helper. You are both to leave this train and go
away from Poland."

I blinked. It seemed to me that he had said Gerda
was a spy, and I was helping her, but that, I knew,
could not be. I looked around at the people in the
compartment. Their faces showed horror, terror, sur-

prise, and excitement. I smiled feebly, shrugged my shoulders elaborately, and said several times, in German, "I don't understand."

The customs man squared his shoulders, sneered, put our passports in his pockets, kicked my best suitcase, and said, "Get going," or its Polish equivalent. At this point I woke up Gerda, who, because of her traveling family, is a great little linguist. She speaks four languages, and a lot of odd dialects besides.

"Hey," I said anxiously, "wake up. This oaf thinks you are a spy."

Gerda woke up immediately and took command of the situation. Although she does not speak Polish, she knows a lot of pretty tough expressions in downstate German, and you could see the customs officer knew what she meant when she said he was a lout, a dog, a cad, a rat, an unfeeling monster, a snake that crawls, a wolf in wolf's clothing—viz., the Polish uniform—and furthermore a man without a brain in his head.

On the whole, I feel that this approach of Gerda's was a mistake. After all, customs men are only human, and Gerda is and was a very pretty young lady. Perhaps if she had thrown herself at his feet . . . As it was, she only confirmed his opinion about how

186

she made her living. He leaned out the window, yodeled something in Polish, and then stalked out. In a moment or so we were under guard, the guard being two highly decorated and glistening soldiers with swords, shoulder pieces, and very dangerous-looking guns. It was a shock. I had never been under guard before, and I began to feel as though I actually were a spy's accomplice. The rest of the people in our compartment were watching us like hawks. Obviously they were scared to death of us, but fascinated all the same.

Gerda smiled experimentally at the huskiest man in the compartment, but he just turned quite white and looked at the ceiling. You could see he was sorry for us, so young, so gay, to be cut down before we had lived at all, but you could also see he wasn't going to do anything about it. He probably had a family and couldn't afford chivalrous gestures.

Finally a man from the Polish Secret Service arrived, a low type of person, I decided at once. He wore a trench coat, as in the movies, but he did not look even slightly like Ronald Colman. He ordered us tersely out of the train, and the rest of our questioning was carried on out in the open, under the Polish dawn, which was very gray and dampish.

From the very first, nobody paid any attention to me. I began to understand what it means to be a dupe. You get shot just like the master mind who sucked you into his or her foul plot, but nobody really takes you seriously. There were a lot of men crowded around Gerda, all of them shooting questions at her, and they kept elbowing me aside, trying to get in closer. Several times I was pushed right out to the edge of the crowd and could easily have run away. Of course, they might have shot at me, but I like to think that I had a chance to escape and instead stood by my friend to the last. Besides, I wanted to hear what was going on, and I kept saying plaintively, "Gerda, Gerda, what are they saying?"

Gerda would try to see around several soldiers' heads and would answer crossly, "They really think I'm a spy. Imagine!"

After the questioning had gone on for some minutes, in rapid German which I couldn't understand, I was electrified to hear Gerda raise her healthy voice, trained in college cheering, in a loud shout.

"Help!" she howled in German. "Help!"

The Polish soldiers all jumped, their eardrums nearly split. All up and down the train you could hear compartment windows going up with a bang,

and in a second dozens and dozens of unshaven faces
and tousled heads appeared.

"I am a Viennese girl," Gerda untruthfully roared,
or at least she didn't add that she was a second-
generation Viennese girl, "and these Polish dogs are
trying to hurt me!"

It was a skillful statement, simple, direct, and exciting. Every Viennese man on the train jumped to
the wrong conclusion. The man in the trench coat
said, hurriedly, *"Bitte, bitte, Fräulein."* The Polish
officials all began to shout at once, mostly about their
honorable intentions. Gerda, pleased at her master
stroke, continued to shout.

Now came pouring out of the train Austrian gentlemen of all sizes and ages, rage in their hearts, fury
on their lips. They carried chessboards, canes, and
assorted other articles, which they apparently intended to use as weapons. You could hardly see
Gerda, because she was surrounded by Polish soldiers,
so I jumped up and down, wild with excitement, and
screeched in my awful German, "Here she is, here
she is!" The Polish army and the man in the trench
coat were thrown into the most pitiful confusion.
You could see they didn't want to threaten anybody,
for fear a lot of people really would believe they had

189

been trying to attack a young and beautiful Austrian lady. Yet descending upon them with every indication of committing mayhem were half the passengers on the Krakow express, all yelling their heads off.

It was a lovely, lovely moment, and I guess it taught that brute from the Polish Secret Service a thing or two about calling total strangers spies. However, I must confess he took a very clever way out of his dilemma. He blew a whistle, whereupon the train engineer held down the cord on *his* whistle and started the train, at a walk. Immediately the wives, daughters, sweethearts, and second cousins of our rescuers all leaned out of their compartment windows and shrieked, "Fred-rick! Come right back here, the train is starting!" Some of the gallant gentlemen hesitated just a bit, but the train whistle drowned out even Gerda's football voice, and in a few moments the last of our heroic champions was racing down the track to catch the train, now stopped several hundred yards away. Chivalry has no place in the modern world, alas.

However, Gerda's ruse did a lot of good. The Polish government, in the person of the beast in the trench coat, was so shaken by the little incident that it gave us our unconditional release, providing we stayed out of Poland.

So presently the train went racing down the track, this time for good, and we were left, mournful and furious, sitting on our luggage in the gray dawn. At this moment a portly gentleman in beautiful clothes came around from the rear and said, in German, "Good day, ladies. May I be of some service to you?"

Now, I know this sounds altogether unlikely, but it's true just the same. I don't have very many peculiar things happen to me, and so I remember incidents like this perfectly. Three other people were thrown off that train besides ourselves—not, however, for being spies. There was something wrong with the Polish visas on their passports. Of these, one was the polite gentleman who wanted to give us a hand in our misery. He was a Dutchman and apparently quite rich. In fact, as I look back on it, he was probably the spy in the crowd. He had too much money for any good to come of it.

The other two people were Finns, and they seemed to be very poor. The Finnish lady was quite beautiful, along Greta Garbo lines, although not, of course, anything like so spectacular. The Finnish gentleman was nice enough looking, but he had only one eye. We called him Wotan, because he was very mysterious about his own name. At first he said the lady was his sister, later on he said she was his second cousin, and finally he broke right down and admitted she was his mistress. We thought they were quite romantic.

We came to know the Dutchman and the two Finns very well, and they were all very nice people. The Dutchman briskly set about rescuing us. He went around and talked to several people in Polish, and then he came back with a batch of railroad tickets.

"We're going to Czechoslovakia," he said heartily, "where I will arrange everything."

Gerda put up quite a fight. She said she didn't want to go to Czechoslovakia, she wanted to go back to Vienna, where she spoke the language and where in those pre-Hitler days people were kind and loved her.

Well, what with one thing and another, like the Vienna train not leaving until ten o'clock that night, we went to Czechoslovakia. So did the Finns. We all went first class and the Dutchman bought two bottles of Polish wine, which is very potent. By the time we got to a town called Maria Nastrova or something like that, we were all quite merry, and in no mood for arranging anything. Instead, we all went to a cabaret and had a very swell time. I had nobody to dance with for several dances, owing to the way the Dutchman felt about Gerda by now and the Finn about his lady, but then several Czechoslovakian college students arrived and after that I danced my feet off.

However, Gerda kept taking me aside, along about six o'clock in the morning, and saying, "Listen, I want to go to Vienna, where people don't think I'm a spy."

"Pooh," I would reply gaily, "nobody thinks you're a spy around here."

"The Dutchman does," Gerda said. "He wants to marry me to reform me. He says the life of a spy is too dangerous for a lovely girl like me." For the Queen of the Ohio State University Engineers' Frolic, this was going far in a few months.

Later on in the morning we had breakfast, still trailing several assorted college students who claimed they weren't sleepy and wanted to practice talking English. The Dutchman excused himself while he arranged things for us. It must have been rather expensive, because he took care of the Finns, too, on

Gerda's plea. Gerda kept trying to decide whether to marry the Dutchman or not, all morning. In the end, she didn't, but for a while there I feared I had lost my traveling companion. We all traveled first class back to the Polish border; the Finns, too.

At the border a fresh shift of customs men popped into our compartment, took one look at a paper the Dutchman held out, bowed ceremoniously, and went away without even looking at our passports or our luggage. That shows you what we could have done if we had been spies. The Dutchman, of course, thought that Gerda turned down his offer of marriage because she was loyal to the Foreign Power that had her in its pay. As we approached Krakow, he kept getting more and more solemn. He begged Gerda to be careful, not to take any chances, and she agreed. There was no arguing with that man. Finally, as he was getting ready to leave the train, in the station at Krakow, he bid her good-by. He wiped a real tear from his honest, kind eyes, and swallowing hard, he threw back his head and said in a low, quivering voice, "I understand, dear. The King! God Bless Him!"

That shows you the kind of reputation England has in Middle Europe.

Mr. Spitzer and the Fungus

THE HOUSING SITUATION IN GREENWICH
VILLAGE AND HOW DISMAL IT IS.

THE first six months Eileen and I spent in New York we lived in mortal terror of falling into the Christopher Street subway station. Every time a train roared by, some three feet under our wooden floor, all our dishes rattled, vases swayed gently, and startled guests dropped drinks.

We rented that basement apartment originally because we were putty in the hands of Mr. Spitzer, our landlord. He was a large, handsome, ferocious man who wrote poems and painted pictures when he wasn't terrorizing his female tenants. He showed us the dismal one-room apartment in the cellar, and while we whispered about the possibilities of roaches, he thundered, "Note the beautiful white fireplace, the built-in bookshelves, and the comfortable day-beds." Eileen finally murmured she thought we would look further.

"Let me tell you," Mr. Spitzer roared, staring at us both with angry black eyes, "this is the best value for your money you'll get in New York."

We signed the lease in a daze, feeling that the housing situation in New York must be terrible indeed if this was the best we could get for forty-five dollars a month.

The first week after we moved in, a pleasure-loving robber came to our apartment and stole our small radio, a bottle of gin, and four milk bottles. The milk bottles hurt. We were saving them up for subway fare against the dismal morning when neither of us would have a nickel to get to work.

We didn't tell Mr. Spitzer about our first robbery; he was away in the country, painting a picture. But when somebody stole all our good dishes and my new hat, we marched firmly up to Mr. Spitzer's little business office in the apartment building, where our versatile landlord made out rent bills, wrote letters refusing to replace old, broken-down stoves, and composed some of his worst poems. We suggested, haltingly, that he check the passkey situation. He was indignant.

"What are you *in*sinuating?" he shouted. We hung our heads and slunk away.

Eileen and I began to hate Mr. Spitzer the day we discovered our fungus. Our fungus grew from the bathroom ceiling. It was a horrid green color, very slimy and nasty. Every night we cut it down with Eileen's manicure scissors, and every morning it was long enough to braid. Eileen thought there was something shameful about the fungus, and she always carefully cut it down before we had a party. If the party lasted until after midnight, the last of the guests would be sure to spot a greenish haze on the low-slung ceiling.

Mr. Spitzer adopted a cynical, taunting attitude about that fungus. "I think it's sort of pretty," he growled, after we had lured him down to our apartment to behold the worst. He said we ought to be glad to observe nature at first hand.

We lived in a symphony of noise. The subway trains, of course, blotted out all conversation every three or four minutes. The windows of our quaint little cave were smack on the street. Village urchins ran sticks across the iron window bars, creating a realistic imitation of machine-gun fire. The man upstairs beat his wife, or maybe it was his old mother, regularly, and she was no Christian saint to suffer in silence; she howled.

But on the whole it wasn't the noise, it was the general insecurity of life in our damp little home that made us brave Mr. Spitzer and try to break the lease. For one thing, it was a very dull evening that some blithe soul didn't bend over and shout through our carefully drawn window curtains, "Yoo-hoooo, who lives there?" We learned to endure these queries from the outer world in silence, for the first time

Eileen replied with an excited soprano, "You go away from there," the results were appalling.

"Ah," replied the thick voice behind the curtains, "a dame!" We could hear him literally licking his chops. All that separated us from this menace was a bit of glass, a few rusty old iron bars, and three feet. We trembled in each other's arms while our unseen suitor merrily wooed us in accents both drunken and bawdy for all of fifteen minutes.

When we went to bed, we had to choose between fresh air and insults. If we opened the window and drew the curtains, the street lights illuminated the peaceful scene of two weary sisters sleeping on two equally hard daybeds. Sooner or later, as dawn approached, some merry gentleman on his way home after a visit to one of the night clubs on Sheridan Square would spot this innocent sight, and shout, "Hi-ya, babes!" After the first month we did without fresh air except on Monday and Tuesday nights, which are dull in the Village.

Then, our neighbors added nothing to the quiet enjoyment of life. Eileen, who is sentimental, spent a whole year feeling that we ought to get the Humane Society on the man who beat his wife. Next to the wife-beater lived Georgie, an amiable ex-football star, and his girl. Georgie was a vast rock of a man with a red face and enough hair on his chest to stuff a pillow. The hair was clearly visible to all the tenants, because Georgie seldom wore anything but basketball shorts and tennis shoes, even in the dead of winter.

He spent most of his day doing the ironing for his small household. He was a neat, slow, generous ironer. He offered to do our ironing once, for nothing, but he drew the line at washing. He said that was women's work. Georgie's failing was drink, and because of it Georgie's girl had the job while Georgie stayed home, quite content, and pottered around with the ironing board, a cookbook, and a bottle of gin.

After a couple of bleak months in New York, Eileen and I gathered up, at literary teas and New Theatre League dances, what is technically known as a bevy of young men to pay our way into movies and brighten our duller hours. Mr. Spitzer's dismal little cave very nearly ruined our romantic careers. None of the apartments in that building were equipped with speaking tubes. When our buzzer rang, we were always torn with indecision. Perhaps Eileen's latest beau, in her current opinion a regally handsome man, full of education and wealth, was standing outside, waiting for the door catch to click. On the other hand, that loud buzzing might be only three down-at-the-heel WPA poets, friends of Georgie's, hoping for a free drink. Incurable optimists, we always punched the button for the door release, and as a result our little cave was like a subway station. The only privacy we ever had was when we went to see the double feature at Loew's Sheridan.

One night Eileen was holding the fort, alone with a good book, and curlers on her hair, when the buzzer rang. Eileen tossed her head; she was taking no chances. Suddenly there was a soft rap right on the apartment door. Startled out of her good sense, my guileless sister trotted off and unlatched the door.

On the threshold was a young and handsome man, carrying a beautiful real-leather suitcase. He was blond and wore a lovely tweed overcoat.

"I am very tired," he said simply. "May I come in and rest?"

Eileen gawped.

"Thank you," he said, stepping in and softly closing the door. He put down his suitcase in the kitchen, went into the only room, and threw himself upon my creaky daybed, with a heavy sigh.

"Have you a bit of spirits in the house?" he asked softly.

"Say," said my sister, "you can't come in here like this. I never saw you before."

The young man looked at her. Eileen said afterward he looked so gentle, how was she to know he was a viper of the first water?

"My dear young lady," said the stranger, "in the first place, I am here; in the second place, I am tired."

Eileen sat gingerly down in a corner, sullen. The young man removed his overcoat, looked about our small house with interest, located our bottle of whiskey, and poured himself a drink.

"You go rest some place else," Eileen said.

Dramatically, the young man rose. "Would you throw an officer in your country's army out into the cold night?" he thundered, with gestures.

"Yes," Eileen thundered back. She is a pacifist; she hates soldiers, especially people from West Point. She went to a prom there once and thought it was very stuffy.

"M-m-m-m," said the stranger, settling back on the daybed and staring across the room at my sister with beagle eyes, "a Red, huh?"

203

This made Eileen very angry. "You go away," she shouted. "I am not a Red and I don't like you."

The stranger shook his head. "So young," he said, "so pretty. I heard they were getting the young, pretty ones for come-ons."

"I am not a come-on," Eileen shouted.

The visitor took a small notebook from his pocket. "What's your name?" he inquired in a businesslike fashion.

Eileen told him to go away or she would call the police. The young man laughed. "I am a captain in the United States Army. They can't arrest me," he said sternly.

"Ho!" my sister scoffed. "Where's your uniform?"

"I'm on a special detail," the Captain replied. "I'm investigating the Communists in Greenwich Village."

"Well," said Eileen, "go away and investigate them, then."

"I'm resting now," said the Captain, with truth.

At this point I came home, shouting greetings merrily from the door. Eileen rose from her corner, rushed into my arms, and shouted hysterically, "Throw him out, Ruth. Throw him out."

I was confused. The Captain looked like just another one of Eileen's beaux, rather more prosperous than most. He was reclining on my daybed cushions, holding a highball glass in one hand and looking extremely harmless. Eileen, usually calm in the face of horrid emergencies, was, however, trembling on my shoulder.

"Go away," I ventured from the doorway, feeling slightly awkward.

"No," said the Captain.

"Oh, dear!" Eileen murmured, and burst into tears.

I seized our broom. "Now, you go away," I said shakily to the nice-looking young man, "and quit bothering my sister."

"He's a soldier. Be careful," Eileen howled from the vestibule.

The Captain rose with dignity, finished his drink, took his suitcase and overcoat, and went to the door. "Good evening, ladies," he said, bowing slightly. "You have not heard the last of me."

The paint wore off our floor during the second month we lived there. We complained to Mr. Spitzer, but he was untouched. "Paint your own floor," he said, indifferently.

A hardware store around the corner sold us what was to be the first of many batches of paint. It was guaranteed to dry in three hours, and I suppose it would have, normally. Life was a bit damp in our cellar. After all, we raised fungus in the bathroom. We painted our way to bed that first night, leaning out from our daybeds to put a last lick on a stray footprint.

Next morning we awoke, expecting to leap out on a shiny and beautiful floor. The paint was as fresh as when we went to bed. So of course we had to plow across the fresh paint to go to work, and the next night we had to repaint the footprints. Days passed into weeks, and the smell of paint never left our small establishment. Eileen got painter's colic and I developed severe headaches.

One night I touched up the area around the kitchen door and backed into bed with my paintbrush. Only after I had turned on the reading light did I remember that the back door was still unlatched. To leap out of bed and lock the door meant the complete destruction of the entire left side of the floor. I decided to take a chance. Eileen was out dancing somewhere, and I settled down to wait for her. Shortly after two o'clock, two men opened the back door and stepped into the fresh paint.

I heard them slipping and sliding down the little hall. I opened my mouth to scream, but no screams came out. Paralyzed with fright, I lay clutching my book, waiting for the worst. The two men cursed the paint loudly.

"This is a bum joint," one of them growled. They appeared in the doorway, a Mutt-and-Jeff combination, a tall, thin, morose man and a short, fat, morose man. At this point my voice returned. I screamed lustily, several times.

"What's the matter with that dame?" said the tall man with disgust.

The short, fat man peered at me. I screamed again, furiously, but without hope. In that building, a scream would be put down to hilarity, not panic, providing, of course, that anybody noticed it.

The fat man said, "Aw, that ain't Elizabeth. Elizabeth's got sort of red hair."

"Oh," said the tall man. They disappeared from the door, and I heard them slipping and sliding over my fresh paint, out the hall into the street.

The next day Eileen and I went to Mr. Spitzer

and told him we wanted to move; we couldn't stand the neighborhood. He was very angry. He said poets had lived in his building, and also that a man had written a play about the apartment house. The play ran only two nights, but Mr. Spitzer felt the critics killed it. Mr. Spitzer said we should be proud to live in this apartment house.

The fungus began to grow faster and faster, and then the weather turned very cold and the heat proved very inadequate indeed. In fact, for three successive days the temperature hovered around forty in our little home. Our friends were jubilant. They told us the lease was practically broken.

We called Mr. Spitzer in to prove our point. He came bustling in the door, shouting, "What's all this about it being cold down here?" He tore off his overcoat with a mighty gesture. Eileen and I, in our heaviest coats, with mufflers, galoshes, and gloves, were huddled around the fireplace. Mr. Spitzer said heartily, "My, my! I didn't know the modern woman was a weakling."

There was a pause. We were too full of bitterness to reply, except to sneeze loudly. Then Mr. Spitzer put his overcoat back on and said softly that he would reduce the rent five dollars.

"How about the fungus?" Eileen said coldly.

Mr. Spitzer stepped into the bathroom and examined our luxuriant foliage. "You don't like this pretty green stuff?" he shouted.

"I *hate* it," Eileen said, almost in tears.

"M-m-m-m," Mr. Spitzer replied. He came back to the fireplace and warmed his hands. Then, in the tone of a man who has tried hard to please and been cruelly rebuffed, "Very *well*. If you don't like the fungus, I shall get rid of it."

We stayed. We forgot to have Mr. Spitzer put the rent reduction and the anti-fungus agreement in writing, but we promptly knocked five dollars off our monthly rent payments. Mr. Spitzer, though, did not cure the bathroom of its horrid growth. The janitor came around one day and put some iodine on the fungus, but it only grew faster after that.

After we moved out, the next October, Mr. Spitzer sued us for the total amount of the rent reduction. We wrote several harsh letters calling him a louse and blackguard, but his only reply was a letter from his lawyer threatening to sue us for libel as well as back rent. We had to pay him.

Last summer we saw him in the Grand Central station. Mr. Spitzer, as usual, got the drop on us. He

209

came right over and seized my sister's limp hand, shaking it enthusiastically.

"How are you?" he shouted. "Why don't you and your sister drop around, and I'll show you some two-room apartments?"

Eileen made faint rattling noises in her throat, but no insults came out.

"Apartments without fungus," said Mr. Spitzer merrily, and dashed off to make the Westport express.

Beware the Brazilian Navy

ALMOST THE WORST THING THAT EVER
HAPPENED TO US.

I ONCE had a perfectly frightful experience with the Brazilian Navy which has made me very shy of navies, especially South American navies. It was just an example of the kind of thing that often happened to me while I earned my living as a newspaper reporter, but *l'affaire Brazil* (which is the term by which Eileen always grumpily refers to the frightful incident) was rather more spectacular than most of my professional troubles.

My relations with the Brazilian Navy began under the worst possible circumstances. The gallant boys from our neighbor land on the equator came whooping into New York during one of those heat waves when people were keeling over right and left in subways. On the third day of it, when everybody in town simply began to go to pieces, the Brazilian Navy arrived in Brooklyn, expecting to be greeted by little children throwing flowers, by mayors, men in silk hats, and bevies of flashing-eyed American peacherinos. The little children, of course, were home with the heat rash, the Mayor was in Washington, the Deputy Consul got lost in Brooklyn and was four hours even finding his countrymen. To cap the dismal climax, all available American peacherinos, like admirals' daughters and such, refused point-blank to abandon Newport and Southampton for Brooklyn to do any welcoming of the flower of Brazilian manhood.

You can imagine, then, the distress and disappointment of the brave lads of the Brazilian Navy when it got to be eleven o'clock on their first morning in New York and no mayors, no little tots with bouquets, and especially no beautiful girls who were heiresses to rubber-goods fortunes, had turned up to gladden their South American hearts.

Just as annoyance was beginning to develop into definite pique, a taxicab drove up on the pier and I clambered out, panting like a dog in the heat.

"Whee!" shouted a manly little ensign, in what I was just able to recognize as rich Portuguese. "A dame!"

Instantly a throaty cheer went up from more than half a hundred sturdy South American throats. Scores of brand-clean white hats went sailing recklessly in the air. A dense crowd gathered at the side rail of the boat, the better to see the approaching lady. Merry cries went up from the thick clusters of brave Navy lads.

My first move was to dig a crumpled piece of paper from my pocketbook and, standing sullenly in the blazing sun, read it carefully through. This

214

baffled the gentlemen hanging over the rail. The piece of paper was a City News "Note to all City Editors," giving the glad tidings that a Brazilian training ship had come to Brooklyn on a world tour. "The crew," said City News enthusiastically, "is entirely composed of Brazil's future admirals and many of the young men now scrubbing decks on this sailing ship are heirs to great coffee fortunes."

Just as I finished reading this interesting document, four gorgeous future admirals marched down the gangplank to the pier, right-faced, removed their glistening white hats, and bowed in solemn unison. The leader of this little band then began a long speech in that lovely romantic language of the coffee country. At intervals during the speech, the men on the rail of the ship cheered and threw their hats in the air. I began to wish vaguely that I were clad in one of those long, fluttery dresses the girls always wear in the newsreels for Daisy Day at Annapolis. Finally the man who was making the speech rose to a terrific climax, all hands cheered again, and a pregnant silence fell.

I dug my battered press card from my pocketbook, took a deep breath, and handed it to the orator, saying nervously, "I'm afraid you've got me wrong.

I'm only a newspaper reporter." The orator examined the press card with great interest, then he handed it to the resplendent future admiral beside him, who also examined it with careful eye, and finally all four of the boys were crowded around it, shaking their heads with anxious curiosity. At last they handed it back, smiled in happy unison, and bowed.

The orator then made another speech, and the boys at the rail cheered again. At the end of this speech two future admirals drew up on my left flank, two on my right, and we all began to march smartly toward the gangplank. I kept looking over my shoulder for somebody from another newspaper or even from the A.P. to show up, but nobody did, of course.

"No speakee Portugee," I said desperately to the orator, who was piloting me up the gangplank by careful pressure on my perspiring left elbow. It was certainly hot that day.

"*Je ne parle pas français ou portugee,*" I said to the handsome creature on my right. He winked, odiously. There seemed to be nothing further to add, so I marched onto the ship in dreary silence.

Upstairs, or above decks, as they say in the Navy, the boys were all waiting for our little party. Cheers broke out as I clambered up the stairs, wiping my perspiring face with a limp handkerchief. Quite a lot of coffee heirs tried to horn in on the orator, and several succeeded. The press was terrific.

"Hot!" I barked desperately, making gestures of fanning myself. Instantly great activity broke out. I was led to a patch of shade under an awning. I was lowered into a chair. Three handsome lads turned up with tall glasses of some liquid with ice in it. In front of my chair several score Brazilians lined up, natty as anything in their fresh white uniforms, and stared at me. Several score more stood in back of my chair and fanned me with their white hats. They made quite a little wind.

Just as I was getting ready to enjoy the breeze, the orator began to talk to me, softly and earnestly, with a gleam in his eyes.

"No understando," I kept saying. "*Nicht verstehe, ne parle pas français.*" The orator kept talking. The men standing in front of me stared with lustrous black eyes, and several of them grinned—wickedly, I thought.

I could feel a blush getting up under my sunburn. Finally the orator took my pocketbook.

"Hey!" I said earnestly.

He opened the pocketbook, extracted the press

card, bowed, took out a little silver pencil and a neat little notebook, and began to copy the information on the card. Hordes of other future admirals crowded around him, but he beat them back with angry gestures. At this point I decided to leave.

"Go!" I said earnestly. "Leave, good-by!" They got the good-by. All hands began to shout, "Goot bee, goot bee," or something like that, and I was marched off in great style.

I was sitting at my desk in the newspaper office, quietly drinking a chocolate soda and waiting for it to be five-thirty, when the lad who prevents process-servers and people who have a plan to end war from entering the city room approached me with what is called a worried mien.

"Say," the lad asked earnestly, "where did you meet the Navy?"

A chill spread through my heart. At that very moment there was a stir in the city room, for five strong, in perfect order, dressed in gleaming, spotless white, the Brazilian Navy was marching down the city-room aisle.

"Cheese it! The cops!" cried the political reporter, an Irishman of ready wit.

While men stood on chairs to get a better view and printers rushed in from the composing room to see what was up, the five future admirals marched to my desk, removed their caps, held them over their hearts, and bowed from the waist. A man in the financial section, far off, whistled between his teeth. Otherwise there was breathless silence.

"Hello," I said.

All five future admirals bowed again and grinned. Their black eyes sparkled and the man in the middle winked.

"No speakee Portugee," I said firmly.

The Brazilian Navy smiled pleasantly.

The night city editor came over and said, "Wow!"

The situation had now grown intolerable. Even the moving-picture critic had been summoned from his office on the third floor to get a load of the Brazilian Navy paying ardent court to the lady reporter. Whistles were rife all over the city room, and I thought them in very poor taste. I would have to get rid of the Navy even if I took them out myself.

I seized my hat, said "Go!" to the Brazilians, and started for the door. A Brazilian immediately seized each of my arms, and three more Brazilians marched proudly and happily behind.

"Have a nice time," the copy editor shrieked in a horrid falsetto.

"Whee!" screamed the moving-picture critic.

Outside the office, I said "Good-by" firmly, and started for home. But the Navy didn't get the idea. We progressed, my Brazilians and I, majestically up to Sheridan Square, creating a sensation of the first water on the West Side Seventh Avenue local, not to mention the excitement we caused strolling along Christopher Street. Grocery-store keepers kept running to their doors crying, "Parade!"

Finally we reached the door of the modest apartment where my sister and I lived. "Goot bee," I said desperately. The Navy bowed, smiled, lifted their white hats. I unlocked the door and they followed me in, stepping briskly.

My sister, who is a very, very pretty girl, was lying on a daybed, her arms stretched out, her hat on the pillow beside her. Her eyes were closed, but as she heard my familiar step, she said, "Boy, the heat's got me! I'm too done-in to stagger into a shower."

"Hey!" I said.

She opened her eyes to see the five future admirals

regarding her with open admiration. Her jaw dropped and she sat up.

"They're Brazilians," I said, waving my arm at the Navy.

"Brazilians?" Eileen repeated blankly. The five gentlemen, holding their hats over their hearts, bowed and smiled at my sister.

"They don't speak a word of English," I said, dropping into a chair and pushing back my hat wearily. The five Brazilians now sat down in a happy row on the other daybed, staring with five pairs of gleaming black eyes at my pretty sister.

There was a long silence. Finally Eileen said, "They're winking at me."

"I know," I murmured. "They do that a lot. They think it is the universal language."

"Hmm," my sister replied.

"I'm so hot I could die," I said faintly. "I've had a terrible day. I had to go to Brooklyn, and Brooklyn is the hottest place in the world."

"Listen," my sister said in a very grim voice, "don't sit there full of idle chatter about the weather. Get rid of the Navy."

"Go away, boys," I said without much conviction. The Brazilians smiled.

Eileen stormed into the bathroom muttering.

When she emerged, all fresh from her shower and with her second-best dress on, she said, firmly, "I'm starving. Let's go to the nearest air-cooled eatery, with or without the Navy."

"Eat!" I said to the Navy, grinding my teeth ferociously. The future admirals looked startled.

"You're scaring them," Eileen objected. In the end, we drew a picture of what we felt looked like a restaurant.

"Be careful," Eileen said anxiously as I sketched. "For God's sake, don't let them get any wrong ideas."

We waltzed along Eighth Street, white uniforms to the right and left of us, until we came to a large sign that said "Village Barn. Air-Cooled."

The Brazilian Navy never quite got over the overpowering effects of the Village Barn, and neither did we, for that matter. For one thing, twenty large, fat, oldish women were having a paper-hat birthday dinner as we came in, and their pretty screams of joy and laughter nearly drowned out the orchestra. Then, all the waiters were dressed in overalls and large straw hats, and there was a real stream of water and a real Old Mill quite near our table.

222

Our little party got off to a sullen start. Eileen kept saying that she never thought she would end up at a place like the Village Barn with a good section of a South American navy. My sister is an anti-militarist. As for the Navy, they were very cold and miserable. They kept making piteous gestures indicating that their necks were getting stiff. I guess you have to build up resistance to modern air-cooling.

Finally, however, the Navy began on their fourth round of rum punches and the orchestra played a rumba. I suppose you might say this was the high point of the Brazilian shore expedition. The little admirals from the far southland were, to our surprise, copiously supplied with American dollar bills, which they kept giving to the waiter, who put them in the pants pocket of his overalls, and to the orchestra, so they would play more rumbas.

Once I retired behind what was labeled a haymow to repair the ravages of several rumbas with Number Three, and when I returned a hideous sight struck my eye. All the jolly patrons of the Village Barn, which apparently gets a lot of out-of-town trade besides Brazilians, were lined up around the dance floor, three deep, jaws agape. In the center of the floor, in lonely magnificence, my sister and the Number One boy from Brazil were prowling around each other while the orchestra played a sneaky, sinister rumba. I was struck dumb by the horrid sight of my only sister doubling for the floor show.

The final blow came when Brazilian Number Two, watching from the sidelines, tossed Number One his natty white hat. Number One caught the hat with practiced gesture, threw it on the floor, and the next thing I knew Eileen and the future hero of Brazil were snake-hipping around that hat, forehead to forehead. It was spectacular. When the music stopped, even the orchestra cheered.

Everybody in our little party brightened up after that except me.

What seemed to me hours later, Eileen and I conferred on how to draw a picture of the fact that we wanted to go home because we had to work the next morning. If you will reflect on this a moment, you will see that it was a delicate situation. Pictures of home and the like can lead to fearful misunderstandings.

In the end, we just marched smartly home, the five brave sea dogs singing some little Portuguese sea chanty in tango time and trotting along beside us.

At the door of the apartment Eileen stopped,

stretched out her arm, as Isolde does in the first act, and shouted, "Go!" The Brazilians all looked in the direction to which she was pointing and, seeing nothing, giggled fatuously. Eileen said grimly, "They can't be that dumb."

"They aren't," I replied bitterly. "This is what comes of dancing around hats. They have got the wrong idea."

There was a long pause. Eileen nervously played with the front-door key. The five Brazilians wore eager, alert expressions.

"They're watching me like a rat in a trap," Eileen snapped.

"You open the door," I whispered, "and I'll slip in and hold it for you."

"You open the door," Eileen countered, "and *I'll* slip in."

So I did. Eileen slipped in successfully but left me outside with the Navy. The Brazilians did not look downcast, only determined.

It was four minutes before the Navy lads fell for the "Oh, look!" gag, where you point in one direction and run like hell in the other. After we were both inside, the Brazilians got mad and rattled the door and carried on generally. Several people stuck their heads out their doors and roared "Quiet!" and "Stop the noise!"

Eileen finally went to bed with her shoes on, and the egg-beater beside her pillow. We slept but fitfully, however, for the Brazilians resorted to serenades about 4 A.M. and there seemed to be a fight in the hall about 4:30. Things quieted down after that.

When we finally woke up in the heat of the bright morning sun, we opened the door a crack and looked out. The Brazilian Navy were gone—forever, as it turned out. I guess they were pretty disappointed in American girls.

INVENTORY 74

INVENTORY 1983